W9-CZT-704

VISION AND THE EYE

FRONTIERS OF SCIENCE SERIES

General Editor
BERNARD LOVELL, O.B.E., Ph.D., F.Inst.P.

VISION AND THE EYE

by

M. H. PIRENNE
Dr. Sc. (Liége), Ph.D. (Cantab.)
Imperial Chemical Industries Research Fellow of the University of London

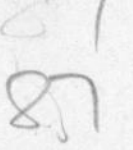

" Hanc igitur mihi operam suscepi, ut haec Physices pars, demonstrationibus Mathematicis ornata et locupleta, non minus, quam Astronomia, inter Physico-Mathematicas partes recenseri posset "
J. A. BORELLI, *De Motu Animalium*, 1685

CHAPMAN & HALL LTD
37 ESSEX STREET LONDON WC2
1948

First Published in 1948

Catalogue No 4/422

Printed in Great Britain by J. W. Arrowsmith Ltd., Bristol

CONTENTS

CONTENTS

CONTENTS

LIST OF ILLUSTRATIONS

PLATES (in art section, between pages 44 and 45).

FOREWORD

VISION is a field of study which is so rich in phenomena that non-specialists, and specialists, too, are in danger of being overwhelmed by a mass of apparently unrelated observations. In this book, Dr. Pirenne has foregone—wisely, I think—the attempt to say something about all important aspects of his subject. Instead he has concentrated on certain main properties of the visual mechanism explaining in some detail how our present knowledge has been obtained. Among the questions treated at length is the way in which the particle or quantum nature of light enters as a factor in determining visual response. Dr. Pirenne has himself made valuable contributions to this interesting new development.

Two features of the exposition appeal to me strongly. These are, firstly, the very clear formulation, wherever possible in quantitative terms, of the basic notions essential to a proper understanding of the working of the eye, and, secondly, the avoidance of arguments founded on introspective descriptions of sensations, which are notoriously difficult to interpret correctly.

Although addressed primarily to the non-specialist interested in vision, Dr. Pirenne's book will also prove, I believe, a valuable introduction for those commencing research on the subject.

W. S. STILES

THE NATIONAL PHYSICAL LABORATORY
TEDDINGTON

4th December, 1947

I DEDICATE THIS BOOK TO

G. H. PARKER

whose encouragement led me to study vision and the eye

PREFACE

THE eye possesses remarkable properties, among which its very high sensitivity to light is outstanding. The present book describes for the interested but non-specialist reader some of these properties and expounds part of our present knowledge of the functions of the eye. For this purpose, comparison of the human eye with other eyes, such as those of insects, is made, and a study of the structure of the human eye serves as a preliminary basis.

The point of view adopted in this book is a physiological one. It is the method of approach of physiology to consider that the living organism functions as a mechanism, that is, as a material system obeying the laws of physics. When light falls on the eyes, the optic nerves are stimulated, this stimulation spreads through the nervous system—where it may interact with nervous activity of other origins—and, as a rule, it eventually produces muscular activity. It is in this general way that physiology considers the events that take place, for instance, when an engine driver sees a red light and consequently brings his train to a stop.

Following this method of approach, the eye can be considered as an instrument, or, perhaps, a complicated set of instruments, detecting electromagnetic radiation within a certain range of wave-lengths. The sensitivity of the eye is so high that it comes very close to the absolute limit set by the quantum properties of light. Its maximum accuracy in the discrimination of form is high enough for the wave properties of light to have a strong bearing on the subject. The theory of the natural limits of sensitivity and accuracy of physical instruments thus must be applied to the study of the physiology of vision.

The eye, or rather the retina, is a part, an extremely "peripheral" part, of the nervous system; the rest of the nervous system, the brain, for instance, cannot be left out of account when studying the functions of the eye. It often happens, however, that light stimuli which are physically different nevertheless produce the same effect on the retina. In such cases, the subsequent reactions of the nervous system and of the organism do not depend upon which of these physical stimuli was used to stimulate the retina. Under special experimental conditions, the same reactions of the organism can then be obtained as the results of different, suitably chosen, stimuli. Much accurate information about the comparative action of different stimuli acting upon the retina can then be gained, even though the processes taking place in the brain are not known.

It may also happen that different physical stimuli produce different reactions in some parts of the retina, but that, at some subsequent level of the nervous system, the stimulations so produced are the same in the case of such stimuli. If the difference originally produced by the different stimuli is thus completely " lost ", no mechanism, needless to say, can produce it again at a subsequent nervous level. According to this, there are not two distinct nervous mechanisms, a peripheral one, the retina, and a central one, the brain, performing fundamentally different functions which can be studied quite separately and the relative importance of which can be debated. There is only one mechanism involving in a single whole the retina and the rest of the nervous system.

As a method of study, it is justifiable to start at the periphery and to follow the nervous stimulation as it spreads from the retina to other parts of the nervous system. One of the reasons for this is that it is easier to gather information concerning the events that take place in the retina than concerning those which take place in some other parts of the nervous system.

In experiments on human subjects, as will be seen, special precautions are taken to keep all conditions, including the state of the organism of the subject, as constant as possible. And, as a rule, the subject is asked only to make simple decisions; for instance, he is asked to report whether two adjacent light fields appear the same to him, or not. Experiments made on human subjects deal with intact organisms under natural conditions and have other obvious advantages. While the conditions of stimulation of the retina of the subject, and his response, can thus be accurately known, the processes occurring in his nervous system cannot be directly observed, and can be known only by inference. Considerations of the kind used in the preceding paragraphs are then frequently used. They essentially reduce to the following principle:

Light stimuli which are physically different, but which produce the same reactions at some level of the nervous system—for instance, in the retina itself—*cannot determine at subsequent levels of the nervous system reactions showing differences which are* CONSISTENTLY *related to the differences between the initial stimuli.*

This principle expressed here in an abstract manner will be applied, explicitly or implicitly, throughout this book and may then become clearer as concrete examples are met with. In applying it, it must be understood that, as will be shown, it is not possible to stimulate the retina by light in an exactly reproducible manner, on account of quantum fluctuations.

The physiology of vision is an immense field of study. Some important subjects, such as intensity discrimination and dark adaptation, have been almost entirely omitted for reasons of space. A number of selected topics is discussed. It has seemed preferable to examine a few definite problems and experiments in some detail, rather than to discuss rapidly a great number of questions. A relatively large amount of space has been devoted to quantum phenomena, which open new perspectives in the study of vision.

The reading of this book may show the value of comparing the structure and functions of the eyes of widely different organisms, and the necessity of obtaining quantitative experimental data in order to obtain a definite answer to most of the questions arising in this field. It will be observed that, while parts of our knowledge of the eye and vision are recent discoveries, other parts are very old. This field of study has attracted investigators at all times. The physiologist Aubert was able to point out—in his *Physiologie der Netzhaut* published in 1865—that Macaulay's epigram on the British Constitution applied as well to physiological optics: " There never was a moment, at which the chief part of what existed was not old."

The preparation of this book for the press has been saddened by the news of the sudden and untimely death of Professor Selig Hecht. I worked for more than a year in Professor Hecht's Biophysics Laboratory, in collaboration with him and with Dr. Simon Shlaer, when I was a Fellow of the Belgian American Educational Foundation at Columbia University, New York. I owe to Selig Hecht my grounding in visual research. The thoroughness of his work in all its aspects has been an inspiration to me.

I am also indebted to Sir Frederick Bartlett, in whose Psychological Laboratory at Cambridge I worked on visual problems during the war; to Dr. W. S. Stiles, with whom I have had invaluable discussions on the subject of this book; to Dr. W. D. Wright, who allowed me to make use of his book, *Researches on Normal and Defective Colour*

Vision, when it was still in proof stage; to Dr. B. Katz, who read Chapter V; and to Dr. E. F. O'Doherty, whose personal interest and practical advice greatly helped me to write this book. I am, however, alone responsible for the opinions expressed in it.

My thanks are offered to the following Publishers and Editors of Journals for permission given to make use of figures and of quotations. The exact reference will be found in each case printed with the figure:

The President and Fellows of Harvard College; Messrs. Kegan Paul, Trench, Trübner & Co. Ltd.; Longmans, Green & Co.; Nyt Nordisk Forlag—Arnold Busck; Oxford University Press; Charles C. Thomas; University of Chicago Press; *American Journal of Physiology; Cold Spring Harbor Symposia on Quantitative Biology; Journal of Anatomy; Journal of Cellular and Comparative Physiology; Journal of General Physiology; Journal of Physiology; Journal of the Optical Society of America; Nature; Proceedings of the Royal Society of London; Science.*

I am grateful to Dr. Bernard Lovell and to the Pilot Press Ltd. for their help in preparing this book and for the care they have taken with the many complicated illustrations which it contains.

M. H. P.

DAVY FARADAY RESEARCH LABORATORY
OF THE ROYAL INSTITUTION
and
DEPARTMENT OF PHYSIOLOGY,
UNIVERSITY COLLEGE, LONDON

March, 1948

Chapter I

THE EYE AND THE FORMATION OF THE RETINAL IMAGE

DESCRIPTION OF THE HUMAN EYE

THE eyeballs lie loosely embedded in fatty tissue, each in its bony orbit. The orbits are conical cavities in the skull. Fig. 1 shows how the two eyes are situated in their orbits. The *optic nerve n* ccming out of the eye on the right is visible in the figure (the nerve of the other eye is hidden by the muscle *s*). This nerve goes through a hole *O* at

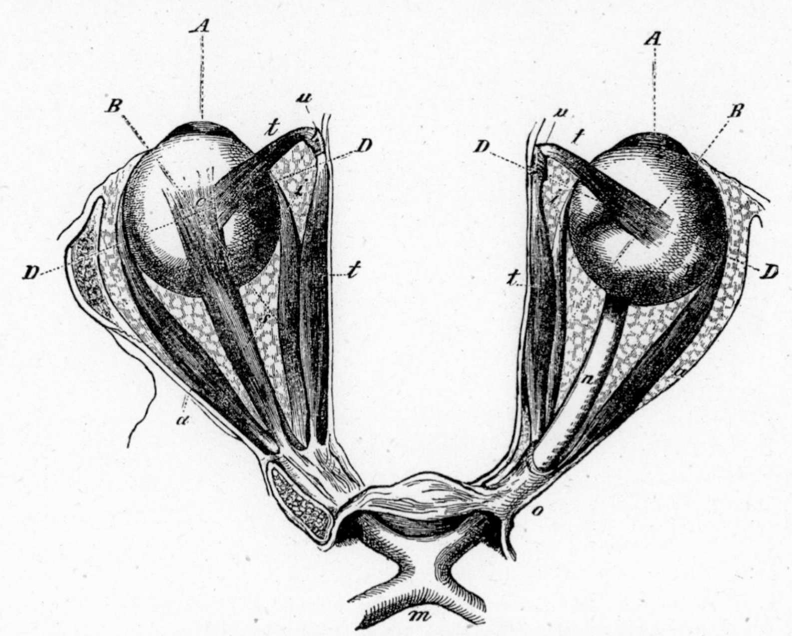

Fig. 1. Dissection showing the eyes in the head.

The dark strips attached to the eyeballs are the muscles which move the eyes. See text. About natural size.

(From Helmholtz (1), *Physiologische Optik*, 2nd Ed. Leopold Voss, Hamburg and Leipzig, 1896.)

the apex of the bony orbit, entering into the cavity of the skull which contains the brain. Here the two optic nerves unite, forming the *optic chiasma m.* The optic chiasma divides again into two branches called the *optic tracts*, which go to the brain. Both optic tracts contain nerve fibres coming from the optic nerves of both eyes. Of the many fibres of each optic nerve, some accordingly turn into the optic tract

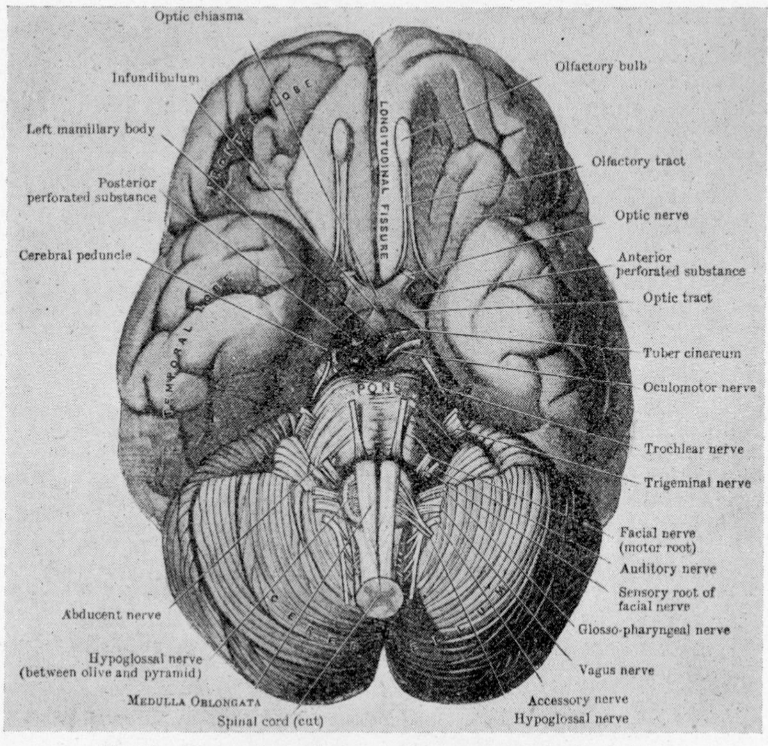

Fig. 2. Connexion of the optic nerves with the brain.

The figure shows the brain seen from below with all the nerves connected to it, including the optic nerves which are cut near the chiasma. If the eyes were represented, they would be directed towards the top of the figure, as in Fig. 1. Reduced to about half natural size.

(From Cunningham (2), *Textbook of Anatomy*, 8th Ed. Oxford University Press, 1943.

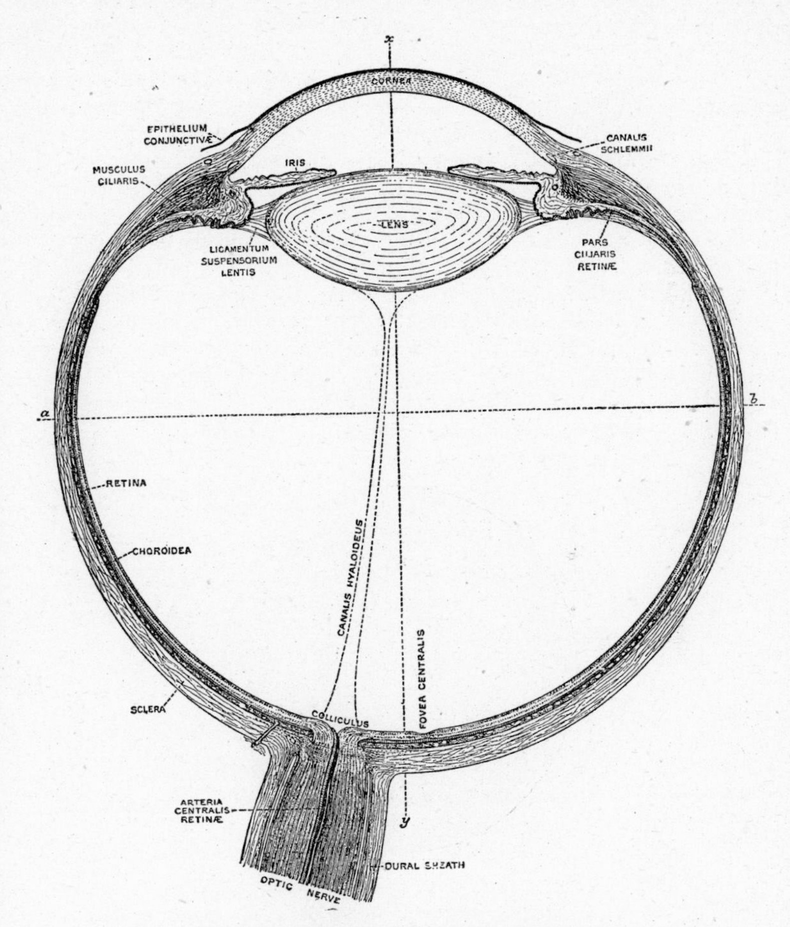

Fig. 3. Section of an adult human eye.

This is a horizontal section through a right eye, seen from above.
Magnified 3.9 times.

(From Schäfer (3), *Quain's Anatomy*, Vol. III, Pt. III, 10th Ed. Longmans, Green and Co., London, 1894.)

on the same side of the head, while others go straight across to the optic tract on the other side of the head. This peculiar arrangement will be examined further in Chapter XVI on the Eyes and the Brain. Fig. 2 represents the base of the brain, with the many cranial nerves attached to it. The optic nerves, the optic chiasma, and the beginning of the optic tracts are seen near the centre of the drawing.

The eyeball retains its shape by means of fluid pressure within it, for it is not made of rigid materials. Its outer coat for the most part is a dense fibrous membrane, called the *sclera*, which is seen as the white of the eye (Fig. 3). In front there is a glassy transparent part called the *cornea*. The greater part of the inside of the eye, behind the lens, is filled with a clear gelatinous mass, the *vitreous humour*. The space between the cornea and the lens is filled with the *aqueous humour*. In front of the lens the *iris*—which gives its colour to the eye —leaves a central opening, the *pupil*, which varies in size as the iris expands or contracts. The optic nerve enters through a hole at the back of the eyeball, and, forming the *retina*, spreads over most of the

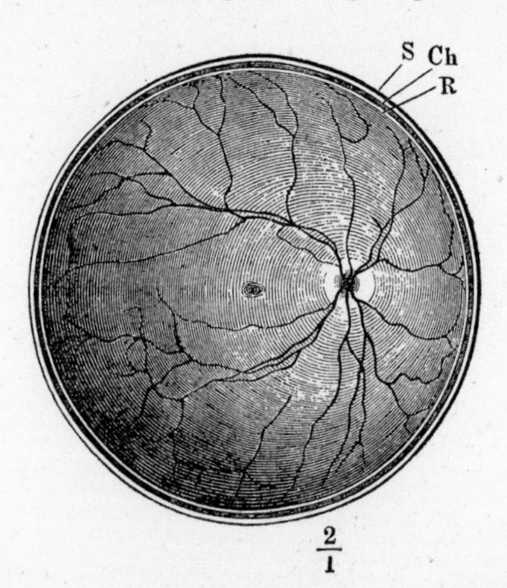

Fig. 4. View of the posterior part of a sectioned eyeball. This is a vertical section through a right eye. The blind spot is therefore seen at the right of the fovea, while it is at the left in Fig. 3. The section of the walls shows the sclera *S*, the choroid *Ch* and the retina *R*. See text. Twice the natural size.

(From Helmholtz (4), *Vorträge und Reden*, 1st Vol. Fr. Vieweg und Sohn, Brunswick, 1884.)

interior surface of the eye, next to the vitreous humour. The *choroid* is a membrane containing many blood-vessels, situated between the fibrous sclera and the retina.

The *fovea centralis* is a depression in the retina, situated near the optic axis *xy* of the eye, and which, although it is only a fraction of a millimetre in diameter, is of the greatest importance. It is this small

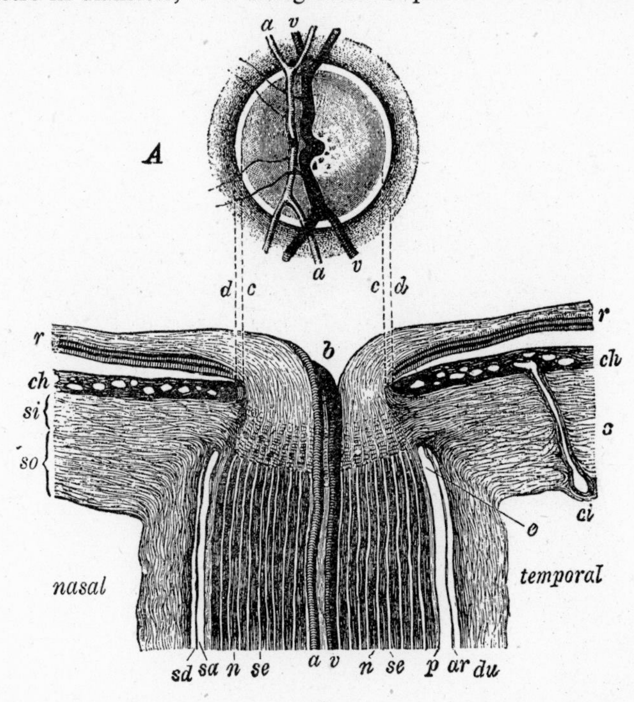

Fig. 5. Section of the wall of the eyeball at the blind spot (B).

On either side of the blind spot, the retina *r* stops at the end of the vertical lines *d*. *Ch*, choroid; *s*, sclerotic coat; *n*, nerve bundles forming the optic nerve; *a*, *v*, central artery and vein.

The upper drawing (*A*) shows the appearance of the blind spot as seen with the ophthalmoscope (see end of chapter).

Magnified about 10 times.

(From Schäfer (3), *Quain's Anotomy*, Vol. III, Pt. III, 10th Ed. Longmans, Green and Co., London, 1894.)

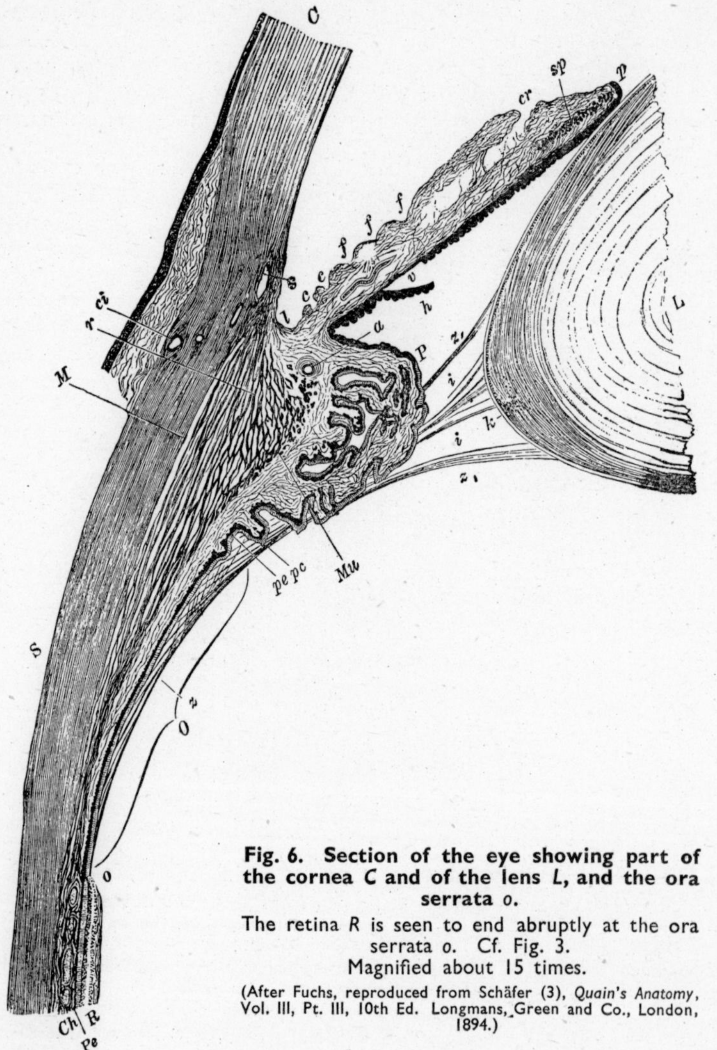

Fig. 6. Section of the eye showing part of the cornea *C* and of the lens *L*, and the ora serrata *o*.

The retina *R* is seen to end abruptly at the ora serrata *o*. Cf. Fig. 3.
Magnified about 15 times.

(After Fuchs, reproduced from Schäfer (3), *Quain's Anatomy*, Vol. III, Pt. III, 10th Ed. Longmans, Green and Co., London, 1894.)

region which gives the most accurate vision of details in daylight. On to this region we cause to fall by involuntary eye-movements, the image of any object towards which we " direct our gaze ". The fovea centralis is in the centre of a region of the retina, about 1.5 mm. in diameter, which has the peculiarity of containing a yellow pigment, for which reason it is referred to as the *yellow spot*. If an equatorial section of the eye is made along the line *ab* of Fig. 3, the back part of the eye appears as in Fig. 4. In the centre the yellow spot and the fovea are visible, but by far the most conspicuous part is the entrance of the optic nerve, the *blind spot*. From the blind spot radiate arteries and veins which run over the whole retina, except the fovea centralis. Fig. 5 shows a detailed drawing of a section of the blind spot. The retina extends as far as the *ora serrata*, remarkably close to the lens. Fig. 6 shows that the retina *R* stops rather suddenly in this region, just as it is seen to stop where the optic nerve enters, forming the blind spot, in Fig. 5.

FORMATION OF THE RETINAL IMAGE

The human eye acts like a *camera obscura*, an image of the objects outside being formed on the retina by the transparent refracting media of the eye. The essential principle is the same as in a photographic camera, but there are nevertheless important differences, so that this analogy must not be pressed too far.

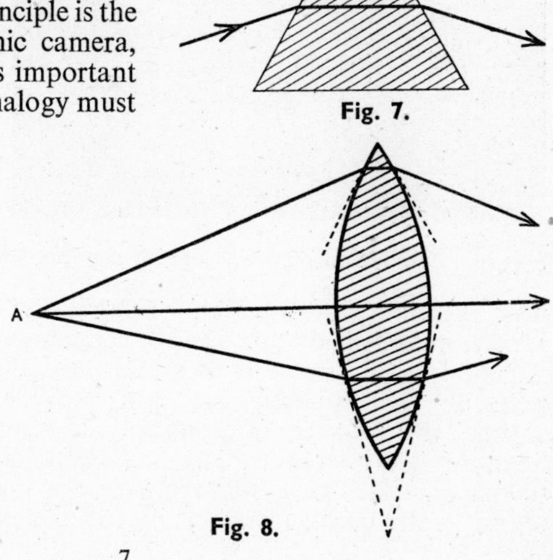

Fig. 7.

Fig. 8.

As is well known, a glass prism in air will bend a ray of light falling on it. The ray of light is deviated from its course on entering the prism and emerging from it into the air, as shown in Fig. 7. Now a convex glass lens in air acts upon light like a series of prisms, defined by the planes tangent to the surface of the lens at each of its points, as shown in Fig. 8. Let us place a point source of light at a point A along the axis of the lens. This source emits rays of light in all directions of space. The ray travelling along the axis and striking the centre of the lens is not deviated from its path, whereas the others are deviated on striking the lens, the more so the farther they strike it from the centre. This is so because the angle of the elementary prisms of which the lens can be imagined to be constituted is larger near the edge than

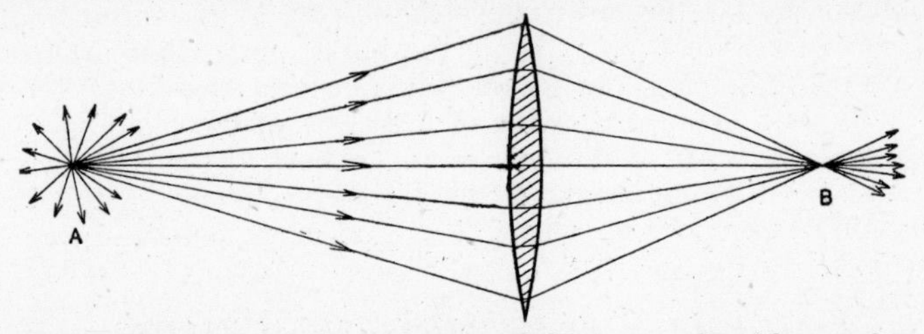

Fig. 9. Focusing by a lens of some of the rays emitted by a point source A.

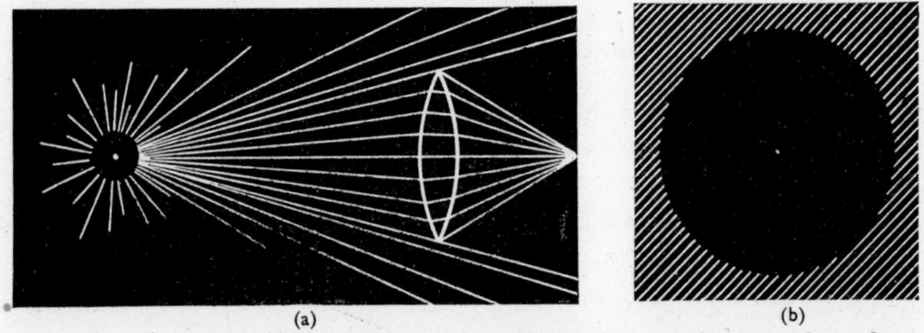

Fig. 10. Formation of the image of a point source on a screen by a lens.

near the centre of the lens. The rays of light diverging from the source are thus made to converge again after passing through the lens. A good lens (illustrated by Fig. 9) will make such rays converge on one point, B. Consequently, if a sheet of paper is placed in a dark room at a suitable distance on the other side of the lens from the source of light, a bright punctiform image of the point source will be formed on the paper. All the rays falling from the source on to the lens are re-united at the bright image (Fig. 10a), which means that no light can reach the circular region which corresponds to the shadow of the lens cast upon the paper by the point source, so that the bright central image is surrounded by a dark circle (Fig. 10b). Outside this circle, the paper is illuminated directly by the source in an even manner without the formation of any image.

This is the way the image of a point source is formed on the plate of a photographic camera, and in a somewhat similar way the image on the retina of the eye is formed. But it should be noted that the eye, unlike the photographic camera, is not filled with air. The aqueous and vitreous humours contained in the eyeball are aqueous media having a much higher refractive index than air. For this reason the greater part of the convergence of light is effected by the convex transparent cornea, and not by the lens. Although the lens, which, unlike a simple glass lens, is denser in its centre than in its periphery, would have great converging powers in air, these powers are much reduced when it is in the eye, because the humours of the eye also have a high refractive index. But this does not in any way prevent the formation of an image. As shown in Fig. 11, a simple system made of a dense medium limited by a curved surface CD can form within the dense medium at B the image of a light source A placed outside in the air. The case is even simpler, though less familiar, than that of a lens in air.

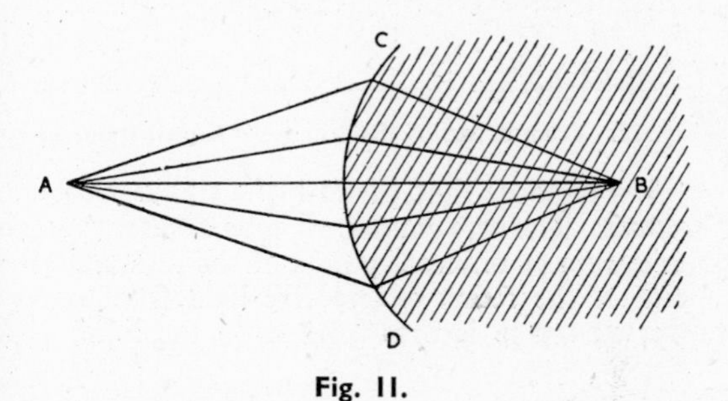

Fig. 11.

Let us consider a single point source of light in front of the eye in a dark room (Fig. 12). The source emits rays in all directions of space. Some of these rays fall on the white of the eye, some on the skin, etc.; the light of these rays is scattered in all directions. But some of the rays, forming a conical bundle, pass through the cornea and enter the posterior chamber of the eye through the opening of the pupil. These rays are refracted by the cornea and by the lens, and are made to converge into a point B which, if vision is to be accurate, is situated on the retina. It will be noted that all the light originating in the point source and entering the eye is re-united in B, so that no other point of the retina receives light from this source.

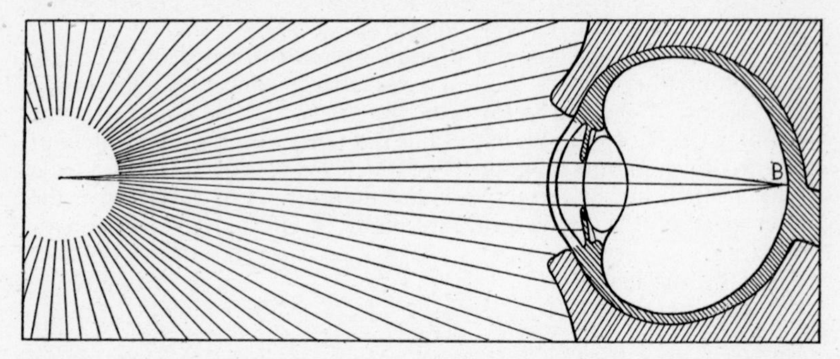

Fig. 12. Formation of the image of a point source on the retina of the eye.

Now suppose that, instead of a single point-source, there are several sources. The rays emitted by each different source converge on entering the eye on to different points of the retina, and furthermore any given point of the retina can receive light from one point source only. A reversed image is thus formed on the retina (Fig. 13).

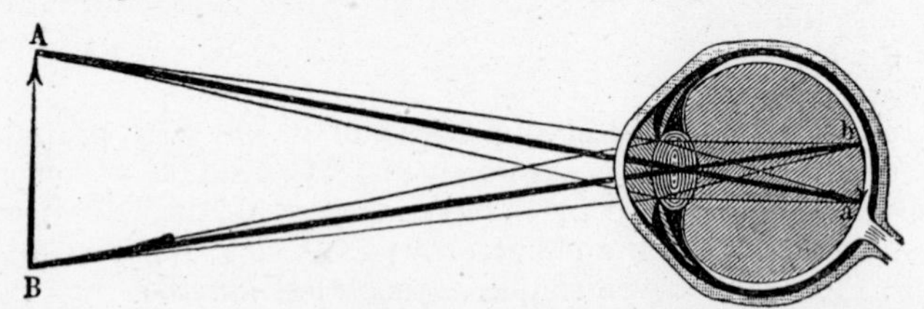

Fig. 13. Formation on the retina of the image ab of an object AB.
The part of the thick lines Aa and Bb which are outside the eye constitute the "pyramid of sight" of Leonardo. (Cf. Fig. 15.)
(From Helmholtz (4), *Vorträge und Reden*, Ist Vol.
Fr. Vieweg und Sohn, Brunswick, 1884.)

Ordinary objects reflect and scatter in various proportions the light falling upon them from any source, for example, from the sun. Every point on the surface of the object thus acts as a point-source of light, so that every single point can be considered as a secondary light-source.

Our reasoning, therefore, with regard to sources of light in a dark room applies as well to any lighted scene the image of which will accordingly be formed on to the retina.

Already in the seventeenth century, Descartes (5), for instance, was familiar with experiments showing how this image is formed in the eye. The external membranes at the back of an ox's eye, for example, are cut in such a way as to uncover the vitreous humour without spilling it. This opening is then covered with a piece of thin white paper (Fig. 14). The eye prepared in this way is placed in a hole made in the shutter of a window, its cornea turned towards objects out of doors in the sunlight, and its back towards the observer in the darkened room. Care must be taken to ensure that the only light entering the room is that which falls on the paper TSR through the transparent media of the prepared eye. When this is done, a picture of the objects outside will be seen by the observer " not perhaps without wonder and pleasure " on the paper TSR.

The picture formed in this way of several objects situated at different distances from the eye, is not, as Descartes already knew, sharply defined for all the objects at the same time. By the mechanism of accommodation the curvature of the lens can be increased or decreased according as the object of vision is near or far. An increase in curvature of the lens increases the convergence of the rays in the eye, and so keeps the image of the near object on the retina. A decrease in curvature, similarly, decreases the convergence, with the same result for far objects.

Even when the eye is exactly accommodated for a given distance, however, the image on the retina is not perfectly sharp. Light of long wave-length, e.g. red light, is less bent by the refracting structures of the eye than light of short wave-length such as violet. Exact focus cannot be achieved simultaneously, therefore, for the various wave-lengths of light constituting white light. This phenomenon is the effect known as *chromatic aberration.* The eye suffers from other defects or aberrations—and has some very peculiar properties which cannot be described here (6). Nevertheless, we can see details with nearly the same accuracy as if the eye were a theoretically perfect optical instrument. Its accuracy approximates almost to the limit set by the very properties of light itself, properties which themselves render perfectly sharp images impossible (see Chapter X). Why our vision does not in fact suffer more from the optical defects which can be shown to exist in the eye is not completely understood (13).

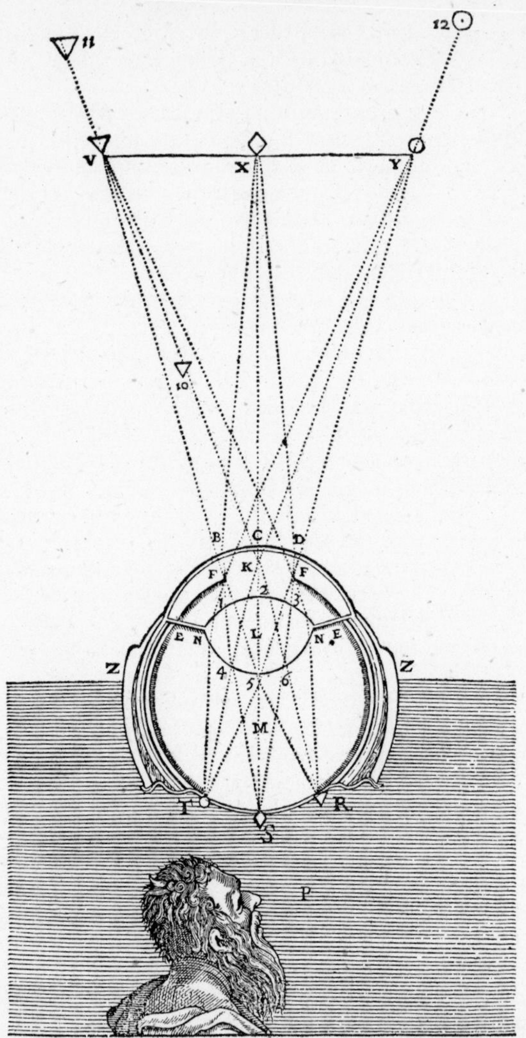

Fig. 14. Formation of the retinal image, according to Descartes (5). Explanation in text. The experiment was first performed by Scheiner; the correct theory had been originated by Kepler. See (1).

(From Descartes (5), *La Dioptrique*, Leyden, 1637.
Reproduced by permission of the Cambridge University Library.)

LINEAR PERSPECTIVE

Although the path of the rays in the eye is in general a complicated one, there is for each point source, one ray (shown for instance in Fig. 13 as a thick line) which travels in almost a straight line from its external source to the retina. It is in general a sufficient approximation to consider that all such lines cross inside the eye at one point, the *posterior nodal point*, situated towards the rear of the lens. In order to obtain the retinal image of any object, it will then be sufficient to imagine a straight line drawn from each point on the surface of such an object to the posterior nodal point, and then to prolong these lines until they reach the retina. Their points of intersection with the retina produce an image of the object. The posterior nodal point is at a distance of about 17 millimetres from the retina in the normal eye (7). Knowledge of this distance makes it possible to work out the dimensions of the retinal image of any given object at any known distance by the ordinary geometrical operations.

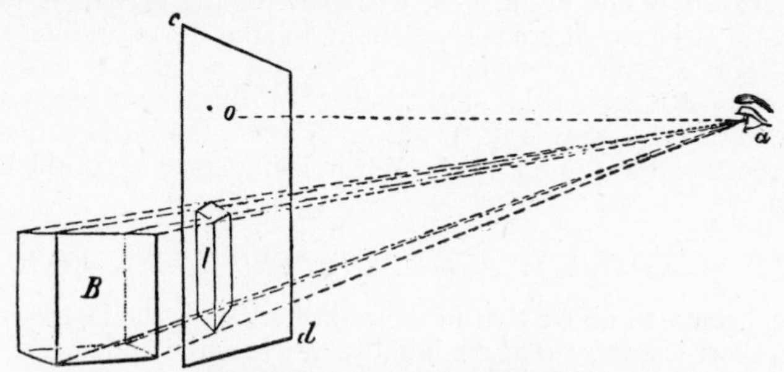

Fig. 15. Leonardo's Window.

Explanation in text. Cf. Fig. 13. The construction of the perspective image remains valid when the eye moves in its orbit, provided the head remains immobile. The apex of the "pyramid of sight" is then the centre of rotation of the eye, instead of being the posterior nodal point.

(From Brücke (8), *Bruchstücke aus der Theorie der Bildenden Künste*. F. A. Brockaus, Leipzig, 1877.)

The shape of an object seen by the eye of a spectator through a sheet of glass, can be drawn on the glass simply by finding the points where the glass is intersected by the straight lines drawn from each point of the object to the posterior nodal point of the eye. Consider Fig. 15, which illustrates the point. Disregarding the effects of accommodation, the retinal image of the drawing on the glass is identical, as far as shape is concerned, with the retinal image of the object itself. In other words, the retinal image of any given point of the drawing on the glass exactly covers the retinal image of the corresponding point of the cube. "Perspective is nothing else," wrote Leonardo da Vinci (9) "than seeing a place or objects behind a pane of glass, quite transparent, on the surface of which, the objects which lie behind the glass are to be drawn. These can be traced in pyramids to the point in the eye, and these pyramids are intersected by the glass plane."* The sheet of glass in Fig. 15 in fact is known as "Leonardo's Window."

Though correct in his treatment of perspective, Leonardo had no clear notion of how the image is formed in the eye. He was puzzled by the fact that light emitted by an object diverges in all directions, while perspective uses a "pyramid" constituted by rays which converge to a point in the eye. It may be noted in passing that the perspective image is independent of such factors as the shape of the retina or the characteristics of the brain, and, *a fortiori*, of the psychology of the spectator. It bears, of course, a definite relation to the retinal image, but the two are by no means the same—the perspective image, for instance, is not inverted. The theory of linear perspective rests entirely on the fact that light travels in straight lines in the air, so that the perspective drawing for a fly's eye will be the same as for the human eye (10).

THE BLIND SPOT. LIMIT OF PERIPHERAL VISION

It has been seen above that in the retina, which is the layer sensitive to light, there is an hiatus at the blind spot, where the optic nerve enters the eye. It is called the blind spot precisely because, unlike the retina as a whole, it is insensitive to light. In Fig. 13, if the point A of the arrow were placed a little higher, its image a would fall a little lower, i.e. on the point of entrance of the optic nerve, and would therefore be invisible. The existence of the blind spot can be easily demonstrated by a well-known experiment. Closing the left eye, look steadily at the cross in Fig. 16, and move the book slowly backwards and forwards. At a particular distance from the eye (about ten inches), the black disk will disappear, as its image then falls entirely on the blind spot.

Unlike the photographic plate, the retina has a very pronounced curvature. It covers the inside of the eyeball up to the ora serrata,

* Quoted by permission of the Oxford University Press.

which is not very far from the lens itself. Accordingly, light which enters the eye at a high angle from the optical axis can nevertheless stimulate a point on the retina, and so can be seen. Using a bright source of light, it is found that this angle extends up to 104°, that is, 14° more

+

Fig. 16. Demonstration of the blind spot.
Explanation in text.

than a right angle—provided, of course, that the gaze be so directed that the features do not obstruct the entrance of light rays. The stimulation of the retina at such seemingly impossible angles is due principally to the considerable refraction which occurs at the corneal surface, as is shown diagrammatically in Fig. 17. It follows from this that a source of light situated somewhat *behind* the eye can still be seen, although very indistinctly. This explains, in part at least, how one can sometimes " feel " that a person is approaching one from behind: his image, or the image of his shadow can actually fall on the periphery of the retina. Even taking into account this limit of peripheral vision, and the maximum displacements of the eyes in their orbits, there still

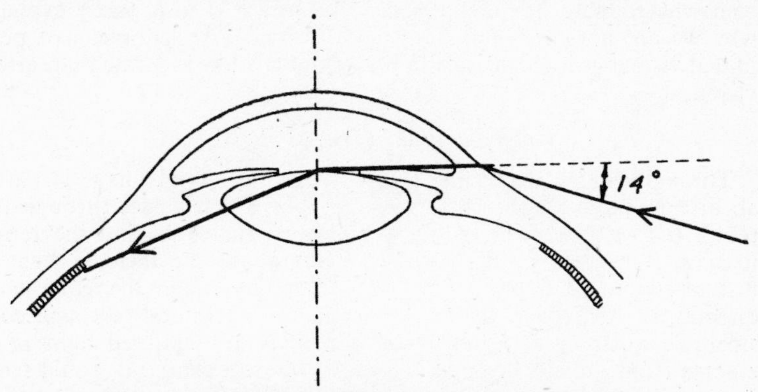

Fig. 17. The Limit of Peripheral Vision (Schematic).
Redrawn after Hartridge (11), *J. Physiol.*, 53, xvii, 1919.

remains for man a considerable blind zone behind his head (Fig. 18). In the case of animals whose eyes are placed on either side of the head, as in many birds, there may be no completely blind zone (Fig. 19) (12).

We always tend to look involuntarily at any object in which we are interested. In this way we bring its image on to the fovea of the retina.

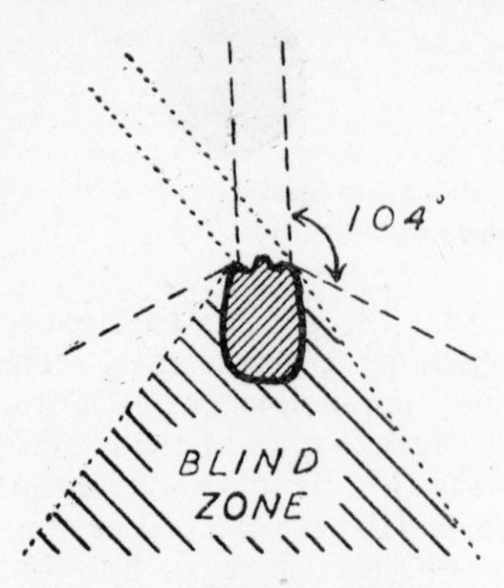

Fig. 18. Peripheral Vision in Man.

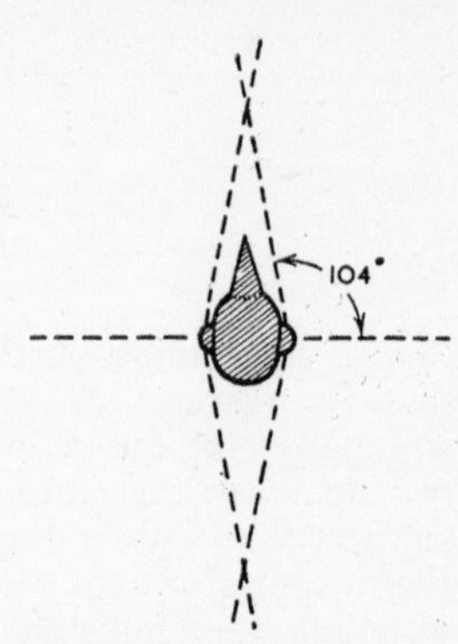

Fig. 19. Peripheral Vision in a bird.

Redrawn after Hartridge (11), *J. Physiol.*, **53**, xvii, 1919.

This fact makes experiments like that of discovering the blind spot somewhat difficult for inexperienced subjects. It also partly explains why we are not more familiar with the peculiar phenomena of peripheral vision—which, at least in bright light, is less accurate than direct vision.

SEEING THE LIVING RETINA

The light which enters the eye to form the retinal image is partly absorbed by the retina. Much of the light which passes through the retina is lost in a layer of black pigment situated behind the retina itself and in front of the choroid. Not all of the incident light is lost, however. A fraction is finally scattered back from the retina in all directions. Moreover, the blind spot is not black, and reflects a considerable quantity of light. Now some of this scattered light must emerge from the eye through the pupil. Consequently, it would seem that we should be able to see something of the interior of the eyeball—for instance, the white blind spot—by the light emerging through the pupil. Yet, under ordinary circumstances, because of the refractive properties of the eye, the pupil of the human eye appears dark and black.

According to the principle of the reversibility of optical paths, the paths of the light rays in an optical system remain the same if the direction of the propagation of the rays is reversed. Consider the case of Fig. 9 where the lens forms an accurate image B of a point source A. The image B can be replaced by a point source of light, in which case, its image will be formed exactly at the point A. In other words, the roles of A and B are reversible without further change in the optical system involved.

When the human eye is exactly accommodated for a given point source, the retinal image will be a luminous point. The dioptric system of the eye then forms *outside* an image of this luminous point which acts itself as a weak secondary source of light. But it follows from what has just been seen that this real optical image of the retinal image

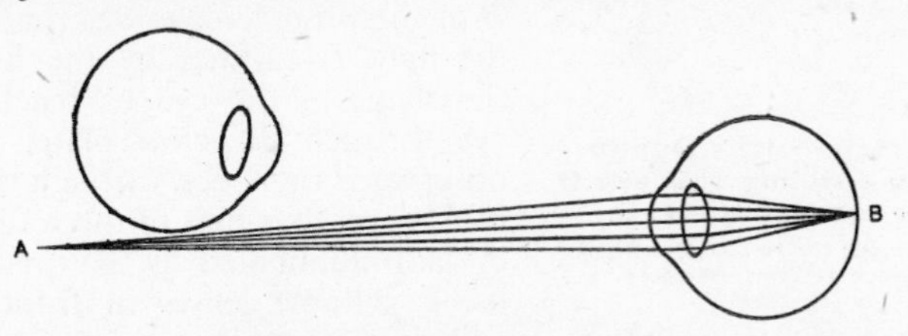

Fig. 20. Impossibility of seeing the retina of a living eye without special arrangements.

is situated exactly where the original external point source lies (Fig. 20). In the same way, it will be seen, if an extended source of illumination such as a candle-flame be used, all the light scattered back from the retinal image of the flame and emerging from the eye returns exactly point for point, to the candle. None of the light can possibly follow any path except that which leads straight back to the original source.

Consequently, if the eye of an observer is to receive some of this light, it must be placed between the original source of light and the pupil of the subject's eye. This is clearly impossible without special arrangements, because the light from the source will be cut off by the head of the observer from the eye of the subject (Fig. 20). For the same reasons the lens of a photographic camera will look dark when seen from the distance for which the camera is focussed, even when the plate is replaced by a white sheet of paper. Sometimes, however, the pupil may appear filled with light. This occurs when the eye is not accommodated for the source of light, for the retinal image of the source is then blurred and expanded, so that the light coming from the edge of it may reach the eye of an observer.

It is possible to devise "special arrangements" whereby the eye of a subject can be made to receive light coming from the direction of the pupil of the observer. A simple method is to use a clear sheet of glass *S* as shown in Figs. 21 and 22. Part of the light from source *A* is reflected in the subject's eye *C*, as if it came from the virtual image *a* formed by the sheet of glass *S* acting as a mirror. The eye *B* of the observer receives that part of the light re-emitted by the image of the flame in the eye *C*, reaching *B*'s eye through the clear plate, *S*. The observer *B* thus sees, through the pupil of *C*'s eye, that part of the walls of the eyeball illuminated by the candle. By using suitable lenses in front of his own eye, the observer can obtain a clear view of the retina, the blind spot (Fig. 5), and other details inside the living eye *C*, as they appear in the case of a dissected eye in Fig. 4.

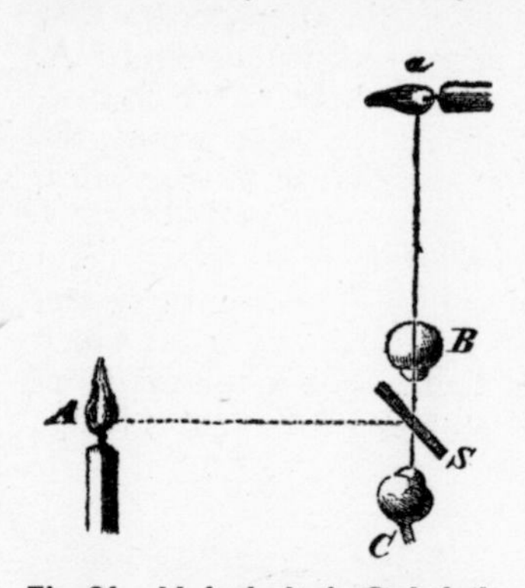

Fig. 21. Helmholtz's Ophthalmoscope, enabling the eye B to see inside the eye C.

(After Helmholtz (1), *Physiologische Optik.*, 2nd ed. Leopold Voss, Hamburg and Leipzig, 1896.)

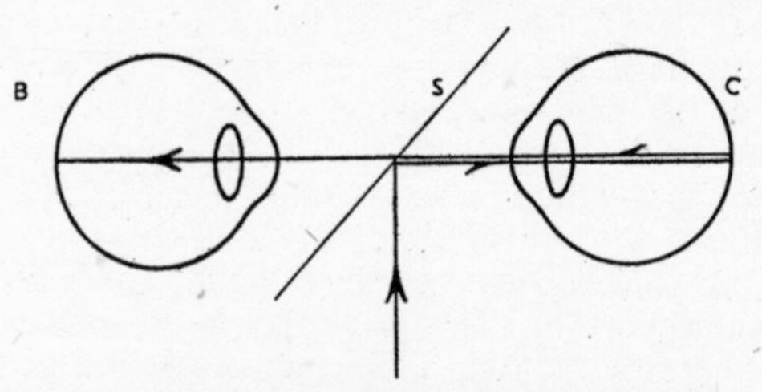

Fig. 22. Path of the light rays in the simple ophthalmoscope of Fig. 21.

B observer ; C subject of the experiment.

The simple arrangement described here, first used by Helmholtz (1), constitutes an elementary kind of *ophthalmoscope*. Improved and modified in many ways, but using essentially the same principles, this instrument is in constant use in medicine.

BIBLIOGRAPHY

(1) HELMHOLTZ, H. VON (1896). *Handbuch der Physiologischen Optik*, 2nd ed., Hamburg and Leipzig. This edition, revised by Helmholtz, contains new material based mostly on the work of his collaborator A. König (see Chapter XIII, ref. (3)). It also contains a bibliography, complete to the year 1894, prepared by König.

The 3rd edition (1909–11) is a posthumous one, edited by A. Gullstrand, J. von Kries and W. Nagel. It consists of the text of the *first* edition (1867) and of addenda by the above editors—thus taking little account of the work of König. This edition was translated into English by J. P. C. Southall (The Optical Society of America, 1925).

(2) BRASCH, J. C., and JAMIESON, E. B., editors (1943). *Cunningham's Text-book of Anatomy*, London.

(3) SCHÄFER, E. A., and THANE, G. D., editors (1894). *Quain's Elements of Anatomy*, Vol. III, Part III: *Organs of the Senses*, by Schäfer, London.

(4) HELMHOLTZ, H. VON (1884). *Vorträge und Reden*, 2 vol., Brunswick. This book has been translated under the title *Popular Lectures on Scientific Subjects* (1904) 2-vol., London.

(5) DESCARTES, R. (1637). *La Dioptrique* in DISCOURS DE LA MÉTHODE *pour bien conduire sa raison, et chercher la vérité dans le sciences Plus* LA DIOPTRIQUE, LES MÉTÉORES *et* LA GÉOMETRIE *qui sont des essais de cete Méthode*, Leyden; published without author's name.

(6) For instance the Stiles-Crawford effect concerning the " directional sensitivity of the retina." See: *Proc. Roy. Soc.* B, **112**, 428 (1933); **127,** 64 (1939); *Science Progress*, **33**, 676, (1939).

(7) For a recent determination of this distance in the living eye, by a technique involving the use of X-rays, see: GOLDMAN, H., and HAGEN, R. (1942). *Ophthalmologica*, **104**, 15.

On the dioptrics of the eye, see LE GRAND, Y. (1946). *Optique Physiologique*, Vol. I: *La Dioptrique de l'Oeil et sa Correction*, Paris.

(8) Brücke, E. (1877). *Bruchstücke aus der Theorie der Bildenden Künste*, Leipzig.

(9) Leonardo da Vinci. *Literary Works* compiled and edited by J. P. Richter; 2nd ed. by J. P. and I. A. Richter, 2 vols. (Ital. and Engl.), London (1939).
The quotation given is in Vol. I, p. 150.

(10) For a discussion of the principles of linear perspective, see the book by Brücke (8). It is intriguing to note that, notwithstanding the limitations of the knowledge at his disposal, Leonardo da Vinci adopted the correct theory in this matter, while to-day some art historians reject this theory and attempt to prove that Leonardo was wrong.

(11) Hartridge, H. (1919). *Proceedings of the Physiological Society*, May 10, 1919, in *J. Physiology*, **53**, xvii–xviii.

(12) Concerning problems of the vision of vertebrate animals, see Walls, G. L. (1942), *The Vertebrate Eye and its Adaptive Radiation*, The Cranbrook Institute of Science.
Rochon-Duvigneaud, A. (1943). *Les Yeux et la Vision des Vertébrés*, Paris.

(13) Hartridge, H. (1947). "The visual perception of fine detail," *Phil. Trans. Roy. Soc.* B, **232**, 519–671.

Chapter II

THE STRUCTURE OF THE RETINA

GENERAL DESCRIPTION

THE retina of the eye is a predominantly nervous layer, about as thin as a sheet of paper, but of very complicated structure. Fig. 23 shows a semi-schematic section of a part of the retina, near the fovea centralis, as seen under the microscope. The various elements look black, as a result of staining by a particular histological technique, but in the living eye, all these cells and fibres are transparent. The light passes through them, to form an image on the layer of *rods* and *cones*, shown next to the layer of black pigment near the top of the figure. These rods and cones are the most peripheral stations in the connexions made by the fibres of the optic nerve. They are the *photo-receptors* of the human eye: they respond to the action of light, and eventually communicate the stimulation to the optic nerve fibres.

A more extended section of the retina in the figure would show its concavity downwards. A complete eyeball on the same scale as the section shown, would have a diameter of the order of ten metres, which gives an idea of the extreme fineness of the retinal structures. If the whole eye were represented on this scale, the lens and the cornea would be seen at the bottom of the picture. The vitreous humour extends from the lens to the surface of the retina, at the lower part of Fig. 23.

The light, entering the eye through the pupil, must traverse the retina to reach the sensitive layer of rods and cones. The retina has, therefore, been likened to a transparent carpet, lying upside down on the floor of a room, the pile of the carpet corresponding to the rods and cones. This remarkable arrangement accounts for the existence of the blind spot. If the optic nerve, on entering the eye, spread out like the prongs of a fork, there could be a continuous layer of rods and cones with their endings turned to the light, so that there would be no blind spot. But, in fact, the optic nerve pierces the retina (entering the eye from the top of Fig. 23); the optic nerve fibres then run on the surface of the retina, next to the vitreous humour, and eventually turn away from the light to make connexions with the rods and cones. It is clear from Fig. 5 of

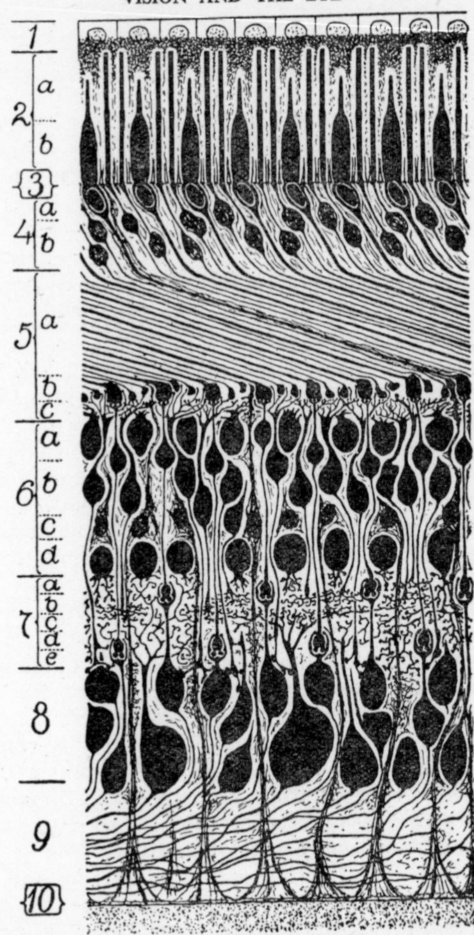

Fig. 23. Section through a region of the human retina near the yellow spot. (1) Pigment epithelium ; (2) layer of rods and cones, *a* outer segments, *b* inner segments of the rods and cones ; (8) layer of ganglion cells ; (9) layer of the optic nerve fibres, which are attached each to one ganglion cell ; (10) inner limiting membrane next to the vitreous humour. For information concerning the structures in the intermediate layers, cf. Figs. 30 and 31.

Magnification about 400 times natural size.

(From Polyak, *The Retina* (1), Copyright 1941 by the University of Chicago. Used by permission.)

the preceding chapter, that such an arrangement makes it impossible for rods and cones to be placed in front of the entrance of the optic nerve, so that this spot remains insensitive.

Fig. 24 shows the rods and cones as they appear in a section of the periphery of the retina. The rods are the elongated cylinders, which extend downwards as fine fibres. These fibres, in turn, expand in a swelling, which contains the cell nucleus, and end in a small end bulb. The cones are the shorter conical structures, attached to a thick body and nucleus, extending downwards as thick fibres which expand at their base. The outer segments of the rods and cones, that is, their endings on top of the figure, which appear darker in this drawing, are the parts sensitive to light (cf. Fig. 23).

Fig. 25 shows the distribution of rods and cones seen as one sees the pile of a carpet. It will be noted that their arrangement is very regular, and that the proportion of cones to rods varies according to the retinal region considered.

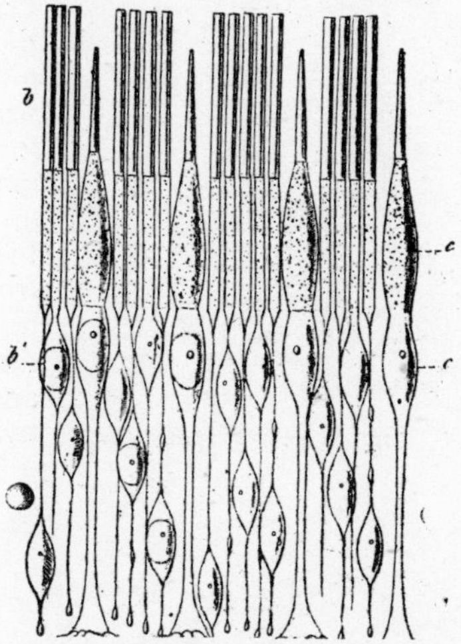

Fig. 24. Section through the layer of rods and cones in the periphery of the human eye.

b rods ; *c* cones.

This drawing corresponds to layers (2), (3), (4) and (5*a*, *b*) of Fig. 23.

Magnification about 500.

(From Schultze (2), *Arch. mikr. Anat.*, **2**, 175, 1866.)

THE FOVEA CENTRALIS

The fovea centralis or, at least, its centre, is peculiar inasmuch as it is the only region of the retina which contains cones only and no rods. The cones at the fovea have a different shape from the cones of the periphery. Fig. 26 shows a half-schematic section of the fovea. Note that the cones in its centre are much longer and thinner than the cones at its periphery, so that their shape somewhat resembles rods, a few of which are seen at both ends of the illustration. The structure and arrangement of the cones and rods in the fovea and parafovea are shown in detail in Plate I, where the gradual change in the shape of the cones, as one reaches more central regions, is to be seen, which shows that the elements in the fovea are cones and not rods. The remarkable regular array of the cones in the fovea is shown end-wise in Fig. 27. This most important, rod-free, part of the retina is very small, being only about 0.3 millimetre in diameter (3). This corresponds to a visual angle of about 1° in outside space—twice the angular diameter of the sun.

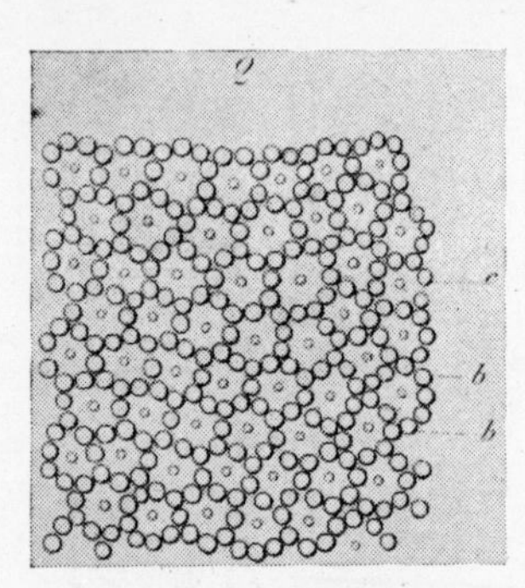

Close to yellow spot.

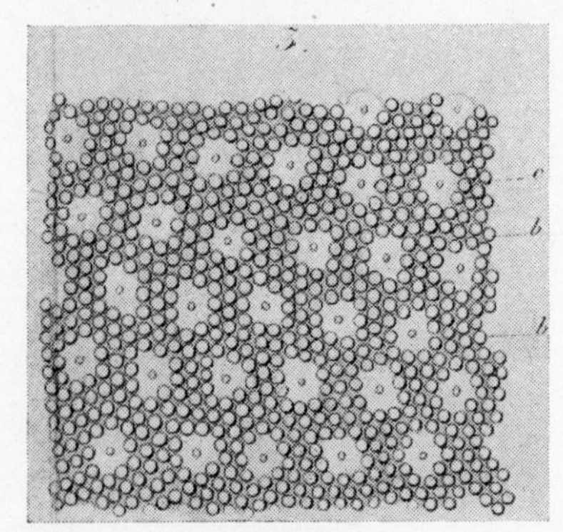

Periphery.

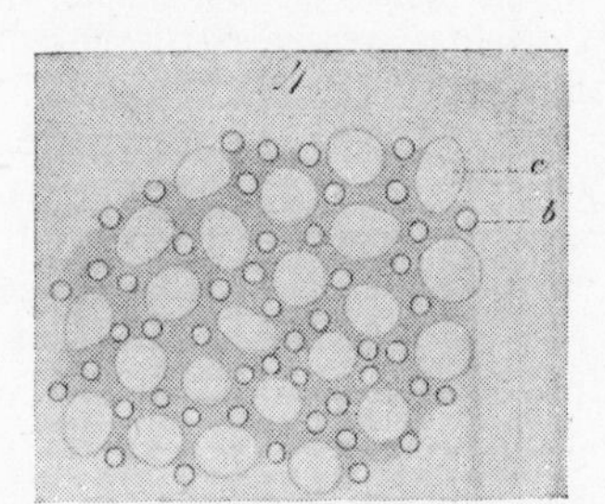

At the ora serrata.

Fig. 25. The mosaic of rods and cones in various regions of the human retina, as seen under the microscope in a fresh preparation.

b rods ; *c* cones.

Note that the proportion of rods to cones is much greater in the periphery than near the fovea.

The structure of the cones is different at the ora serrata, where their outer segment is missing.

Fresh retina. Magnification 500.

(From Schultze (2), *Arch. mikr. Anat.*, **2**, 175, 1866.)

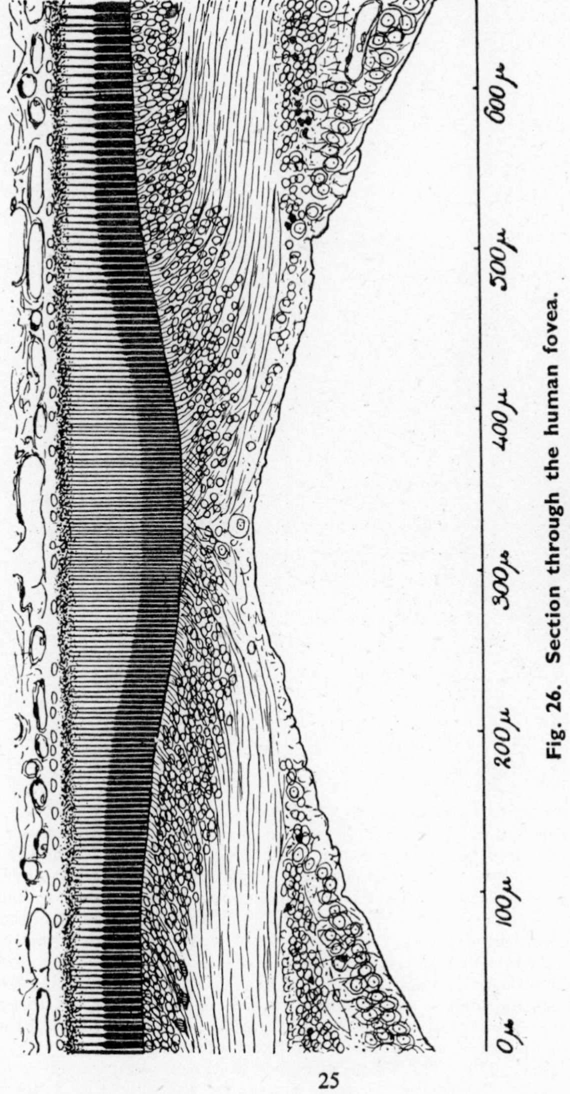

Fig. 26. Section through the human fovea.

Half schematic.

Magnification about 200. Cf. Fig. 28.

(From Polyak, *The Retina* (1). Copyright 1941 by the University of Chicago. Used by permission.)

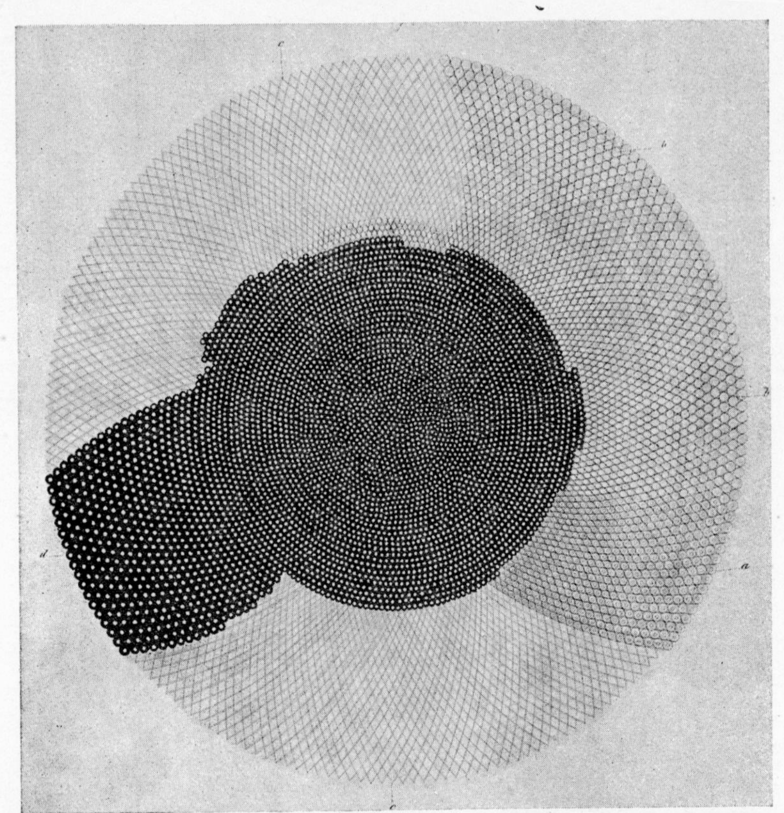

Fig. 27. The mosaic of the cones in the fovea centralis of the human retina. *bb* represents the bodies or inner segments of the cones, arranged in curvilinear rows as a shagreen-like mosaic. In *a* the pointed ends, or outer segments, of the cones are shown as they appear when the microscope is focussed at their level. The principle on which the cones are arranged is shown by the lines *cc*. The cones are arranged much less regularly in the centre than in the other regions of the fovea. The figure is based on drawings made of several fresh retinae. Schultze states that the disposition of the cones is fully as regular as is shown by the figure—provided the retina is in a sufficiently fresh state. The black part of the drawing shows the retina as Schultze supposed it would appear if the pigment were left in position, as in several of the drawings of bird retinae of Plate III. This disposition of the black pigment is not based on direct observation.

Magnification about 270. The outer diameter of the drawing corresponds to about 0.35 mm. on the retina. (From Schultze (2), *Arch. mikr. Anat.*, **2**, 175, 1866.)

TOPOGRAPHY OF THE RODS AND CONES

The data on the distribution of rods and cones shown in Figs. 25 and 27 represent the retina in the fresh, unprepared state. (A human retina can be studied by anatomists when a human eye has to be removed, for instance, as the result of an accident.) The study of fresh retinae reveals the great regularity of their structure, but does not give complete quantitative information on the distribution of rods and cones over the whole retina, because the retina deteriorates very rapidly. By fixing the fresh retina in a suitable fluid, it is possible to preserve it indefinitely, but at the unavoidable cost of some alteration in its structure. The topography of the rods and cones, however, can be studied at leisure in such a preparation. Fig. 28 represents a flat section of such a fixed preparation of a region of a human retina, containing the fovea. The section has cut the inner segments of the rods and cones. Except in the centre, the cones, accordingly, appear as circles which are much larger than those corresponding to the rods. The main interest of such sections is, to give the number of cones and rods per unit area in each region of the retina. Fig. 28 shows that, in this particular retina, the most central rod appears at a distance of about 0.13 millimetre from the centre of the fovea.

Flat sections of this kind have been made for the entire retina. The number of rods and the number of cones per unit area in each region, along a complete meridian of a retina, is shown in Fig. 29. The number of cones decreases rapidly from the centre, falling to a low value in the periphery, but rising again slightly at the ora serrata. There are no rods in the centre of the fovea. Outside it, their number increases rapidly, reaching a maximum of about 160,000 rods per square millimetre in a region 5 to 6 mm. from the centre. In more peripheral regions, the number of rods decreases, but it remains considerably higher than the number of cones. The highest density of cones occurs in the fovea centralis, where they number about 147,000 per square millimetre; but the thinnest cones in the very centre of the fovea, number in all, only a few hundreds. These are the retinal elements we constantly use for seeing the finest details. The distance between the centres of two adjacent cones in this most accurate region of the retina has generally a value between 0·0020 and 0·0025 mm. (3) (see Chapter X). A graph of the distribution of rods and cones in and near the fovea is given in Fig. 37 of the next chapter.

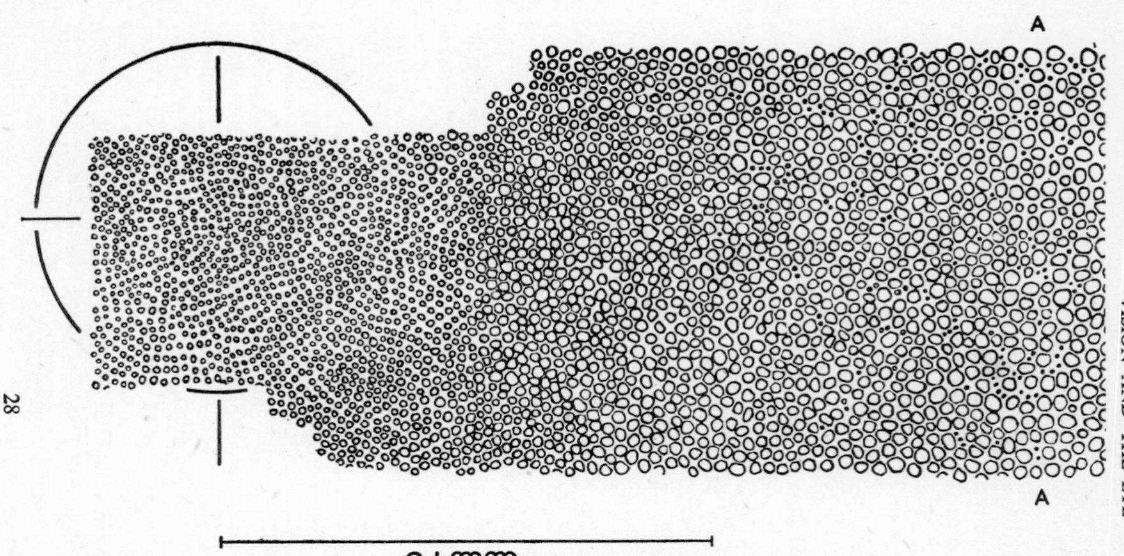

Fig. 28. Horizontal section through a region of a fixed human retina containing the fovea. The scale refers to the retina in the fixed state. Multiply by 1.31 to allow for the shrinkage due to fixation. The centre of the fovea (on the left, top drawing) is defined by the intersection of the three straight lines, or by the centre of the circle. The drawing is continued at the same magnification on the next page, with an overlapping indicated by the letters *AA*. The section has cut through the inner segments, or bodies, of the rods and cones. In the centre of the fovea, the cones are represented by small circles. These become progressively larger as one goes towards the parafovea. In this region the rods, appearing as small circles, are seen in between the broad inner segments of the cones (see especially lower drawing). The first rod is seen in the preparation near the middle of the top drawing, above the right end of the scale. It is situated at a distance of 0.13 mm. from the foveal centre. Flat sections such as this are more likely to reveal the presence of rods near the foveal centre, than vertical sections

such as that of Fig. 26, since sections of the latter kind may obviously fall in between the most centrally placed rods, and miss them. This may explain why the "rod-free area" as measured on the latter preparation, has a considerably larger radius than on the present preparation. But the possibility of individual variations from retina to retina must also be borne in mind in this connection.

(Redrawn at a higher magnification (650) and slightly modified after Østerberg (3), *Acta Ophthal.*, Suppl. 6, Nyt Nordisk Forlag—Arnold Busck, Copenhagen, 1935.)

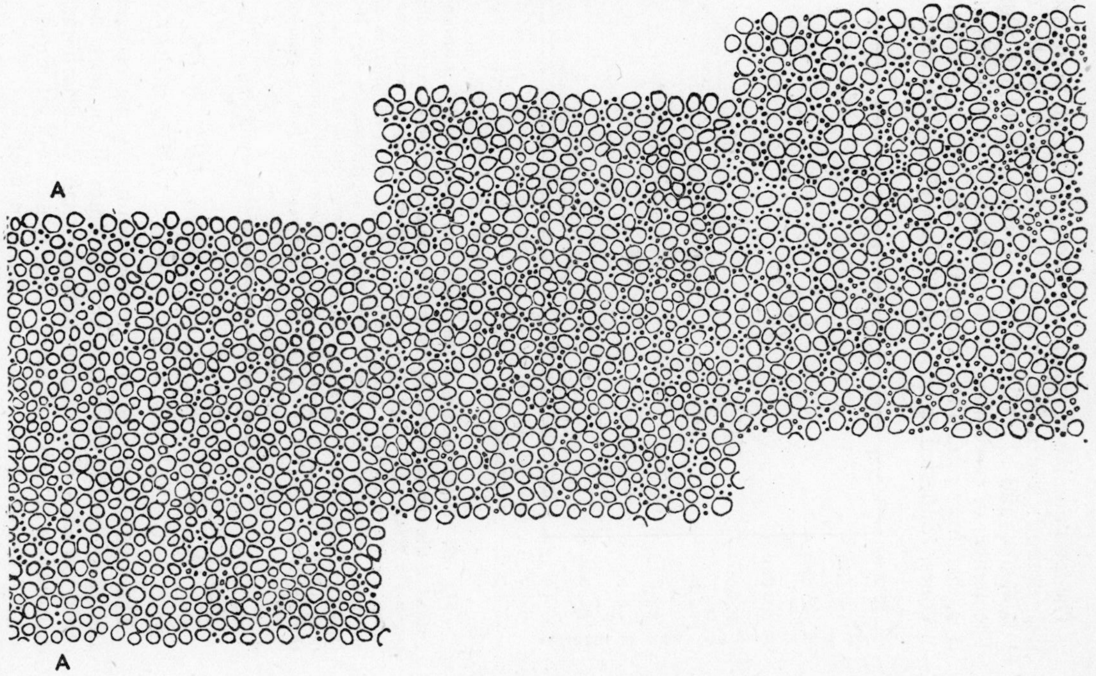

A

A

D

The total number of rods in the human retina has been determined by this method; the retina contains the enormous number of between 110,000,000 and 125,000,000 rods. It contains about 6,500,000 cones. The number of nerve-fibres in the optic nerve is of the order of 1,000,000. It is, therefore, certain that there must often be a large number of rods, or cones, connected to one and the same fibre of the optic nerve.

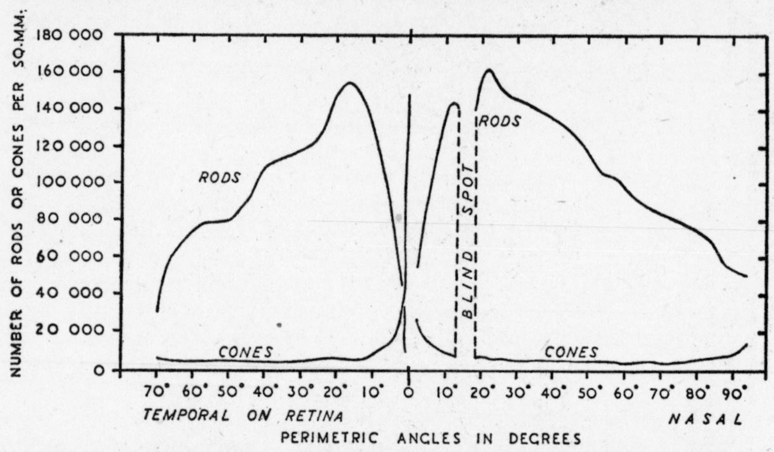

Fig. 29. Distribution of the rods and cones in the human retina.
Instead of the retinal distances, Østerberg's values for the corresponding perimetric angles are given. Although approximate only, especially at the higher angles, such values are more useful in practice than the distances in millimetres on the retina. For the meaning of perimetric angles see the explanation of Fig. 39 of the next chapter. Note that the distribution of rods and cones on the nasal side in and near the fovea, is not given on this graph. It would be approximately the same as the distribution on the temporal side of the retina—which is seen on the left of the vertical passing through 0° on the angle scale.

(Plotted from the numerical data of Østerberg (3).)

THE CONNEXIONS BETWEEN THE RODS AND CONES AND THE OPTIC NERVE FIBRES

The anatomical study of the connexions existing between the rods and cones on the one hand, and the fibres of the optic nerve on the other, presents even greater difficulty than the determination of the distribution of rods and cones in the retina. As yet, these connexions are not known in an exact quantitative manner.

Fig. 30 shows the extreme complexity of the various kinds of nervous connexions observed in the retina. It will be seen that there are many *bipolar cells* (*d*, *e*, *f*, *h*), which connect the rods (*a*), or cones (*b*), with the *ganglion cells* (*m*, *n*, *o*, *p*, *s*), from which the optic nerve fibres go to the brain. The bipolar cells thus may act as relay stations between the light receptors and the optic nerve fibres. There are also cells (*c*), which make horizontal connexions between the light receptors, without having direct connexions with the optic nerve fibres.

Fig. 31 shows the main types of connexions formed between the rods and cones and the optic nerve fibres. *E* shows a single cone *b* connected to a ganglion cell *s* and optic nerve-fibre through a dipolar cell *h* which makes no connexion with other cones or rods. This cone thus has a " single line " connexion to the brain. It appears that most of the cones of the fovea centralis are connected in this way.

The arrangement of the rods shown in *B* is quite different. Here several rods are connected to the same bipolar cell, with the result that the nervous stimulation of the several rods can converge on the same nerve-fibre. When, therefore, an extended patch of light falls on the retina the various rods excited can add together their individual contributions in order to excite one nerve fibre. The system *B* may then be able to respond to light when a system such as *E* cannot do so, even assuming that the intrinsic sensitivity to light of a single rod *a* is not higher than that of a single cone, *b*. We shall not be surprised therefore, to find that peripheral parts of the retina, which contain arrangements such as *B*, are more sensitive than the centre of the fovea, which seems to be made up mostly of arrangements such as E. But this increase of sensitivity is obtained at the cost of a loss of accuracy, since in the periphery the individual elements which detect light are not single rods, but groups of rods belonging to a single optic fibre, such as *B*. A group of this kind will, of course, be much larger in area than a single foveal cone. Further nervous convergence may again take place at the level of the ganglion cells. A very large number of rods may thus be able to act as a single nervous unit and to summate the effects of light over a comparatively large retinal area. Physiological evidence of various kinds shows that such a unit may contain thousands of rods, as will be seen in the section on " receptive fields " in Chapter V.

From the point of view of the functioning of the eye, the main conclusion from the anatomical studies is that some of the optic nerve fibres are connected to single cones while some others are connected

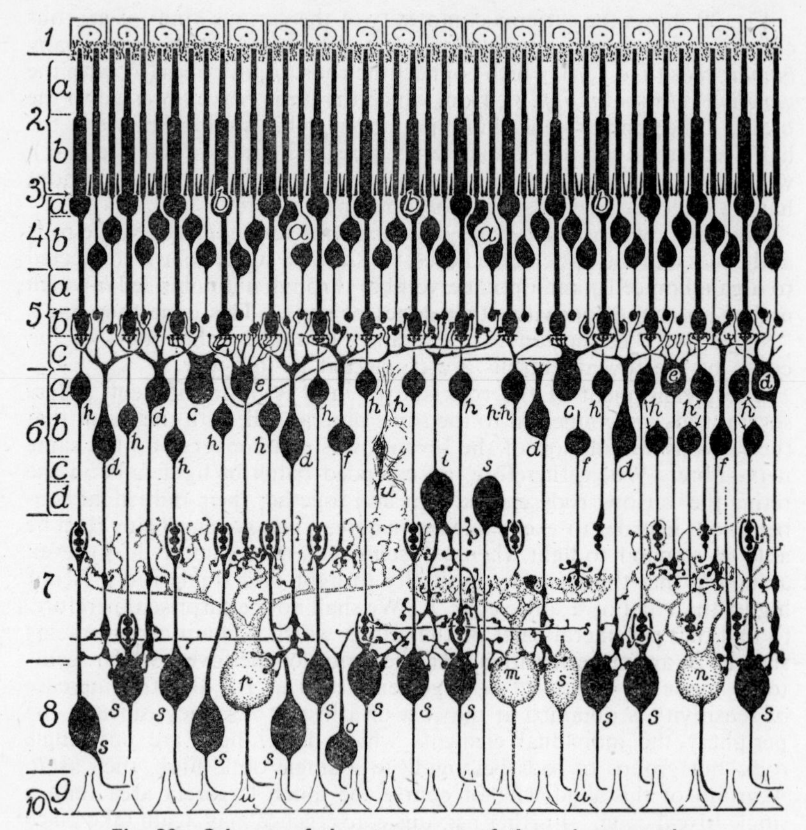

Fig. 30. Scheme of the structures of the primate retina.

Explanation in text. Cf. Fig. 23. Magnification about 400.

(From Polyak, *The Retina* (1). Copyright 1941 by the University of Chicago. Used by permission.

to very large groups of rods acting as units. Intermediary types of connexion also exist, such as that shown in Fig. 31 *H*, in which both rods and cones are seen to be connected to the same nerve fibre.

In these matters, over-simplification of the events assumed to occur in the nervous connexions must, however, be avoided. For instance,

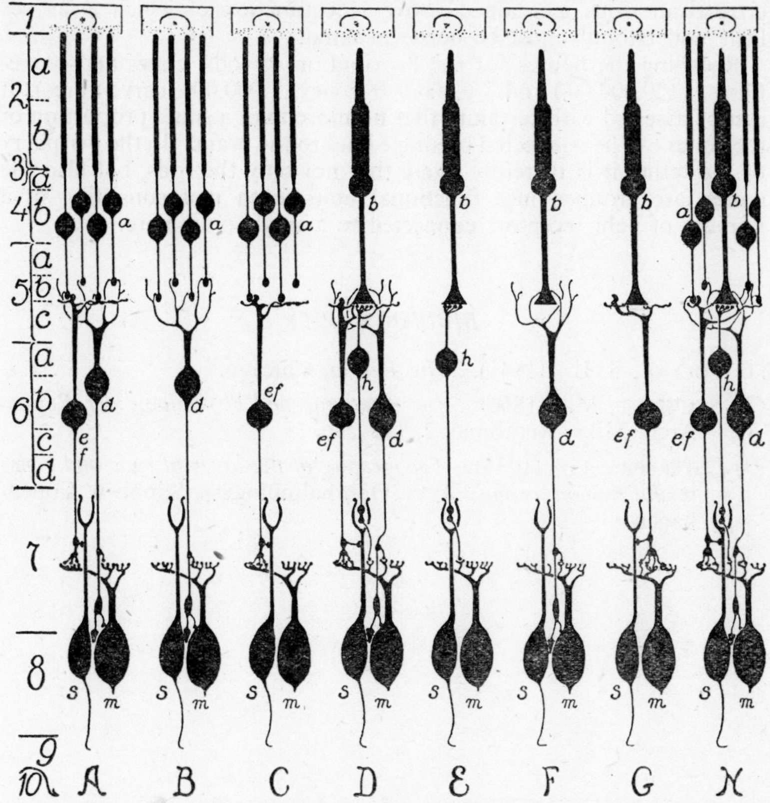

Fig. 31. Types of connexions between photo-receptors and optic nerve fibres.

Schematic. Explanation in text. Cf. Fig. 23 and 30.

(From Polyak, *The Retina* (1). Copyright 1941 by the University of Chicago. Used by permission.)

there exist in the optic nerve " off-fibres ", which respond only *after* the stimulating light has been cut *off*, as will be explained in Chapter V. This shows that the intermediary structures between photo-receptors and nerve-fibre may act in a way very different from that of a simple type of " relay station ". Again, the existence of the horizontal cross-connexions mentioned above—the function of which is as yet little understood—must be borne in mind.

Recalling the figures for the distribution of rods, cones and nerve-fibres, (120,000,000 rods, 6,000,000 cones, 1,000,000 nerve-fibres), it can be asserted with certainty that no more than a small proportion of the cones can be connected by single lines to the brain. In the periphery of the retina it is therefore likely that not only the rods, but also the cones, are grouped into functional units, each unit consisting of a number of light receptors connected to a single optic fibre.

BIBLIOGRAPHY

(1) POLYAK, S. L. (1941). *The Retina*, Chicago.

(2) SCHULTZE, M. (1866). *Zur Anatomie und Physiologie der Retina*, Arch. Mikr. Anatomie, 2, 175–286.

(3) ØSTERBERG, G. (1935). *Topography of the layer of rods and cones in the human retina*, Acta Ophthalmologica, Suppl. 6 Copenhagen.

Chapter III

SOME PROPERTIES OF RODS AND CONES

NIGHT VISION

It is a familiar fact that on a moonless night, our vision not only is very blurred, but is also colourless. Although we can distinguish the colour of some of the stars, the landscape itself appears to be made up of a narrow range of grey and black tones. Even when the moon is shining in a clear sky, the colours of objects are not easily recognized, although the blueness of the sky, the greenness of foliage and the redness of bricks may be faintly perceived. All this is well known, especially to artists. No painting of a night landscape which aims at some degree of verisimilitude has ever been painted with bright colours—although a sunny landscape may be painted entirely in black and white with good effect.

The observation that our vision is colourless at such low intensities of light can be expressed in the following way, without referring to the nature of our subjective sensations. There is no discrimination of wave-length as such; differences of brightness only can be detected. This means that if the intensities of two different physical lights are suitably adjusted, the subject of the experiment will be unable to differentiate between them. This applies as much to monochromatic lights as to lights made up of radiations having different wave-lengths.

Fig. 32.

The conditions of night vision may easily be imitated in the laboratory, by experimenting in a dark room. Let us arrange in such a room a photometer field, made up of two half-fields A and B (Fig. 32), and having a diameter which subtends a large angle, say, 20 degrees, at the eye of the subject. This can be done in the following simple way—which, however, might not be the most convenient way in practice,

A triangular prism AEB, made of plaster of Paris, and having a sharp edge E normal to the plane of the figure, receives light from two different sources, one on the right and one on the left (Fig. 33). The subject S of the experiment is separated from the prism by an opaque diaphragm D, having in it a circular aperture Q through which he sees the edge E and the two faces A and B of the prism. In the darkness the subject S thus sees a circular field divided into two halves A and B (Figs. 32 and 34). By making suitable changes in the two sources of light which illuminate the faces of the prism, the two halves A and B can be filled with lights of various wave-lengths and intensities. In this way let us fill A with light of wave-length 450mμ and B with light of 580mμ. At ordinary intensities of light, the half-field A will usually be described as blue and B as yellow. Let us now decrease the physical intensity

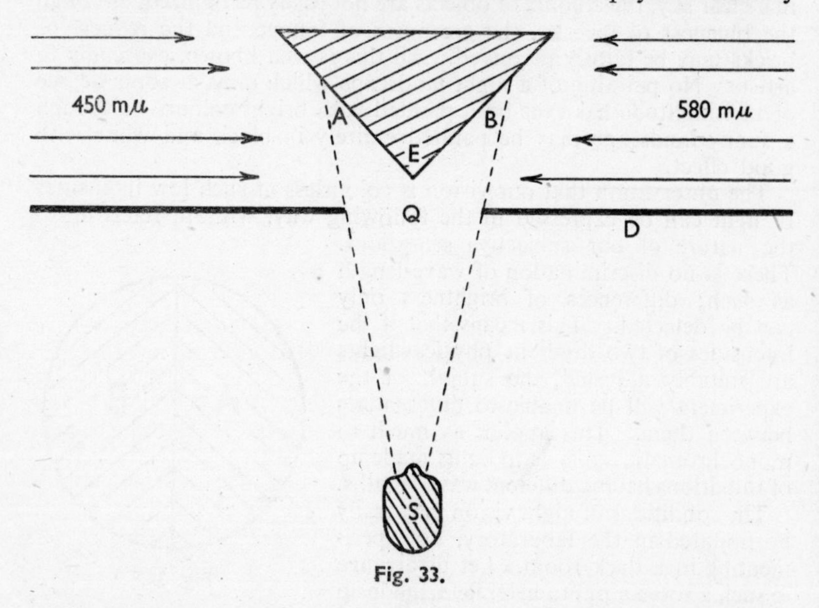

Fig. 33.

of the lights falling on A and B, making it so low that eventually the two half-fields are only just visible (Fig. 34, I) to a dark-adapted subject, that is, to a subject who has been waiting in total darkness for at least half an hour before starting the experiment. Under such conditions it is impossible for the subject to tell which is blue, and which is yellow light. This is also the case within an appreciable range of higher intensities, at which the two light patches A and B are clearly visible (Fig. 34, II and V). As far as the subject is concerned, these two half-fields might be filled with dim white light. A perfect photometric

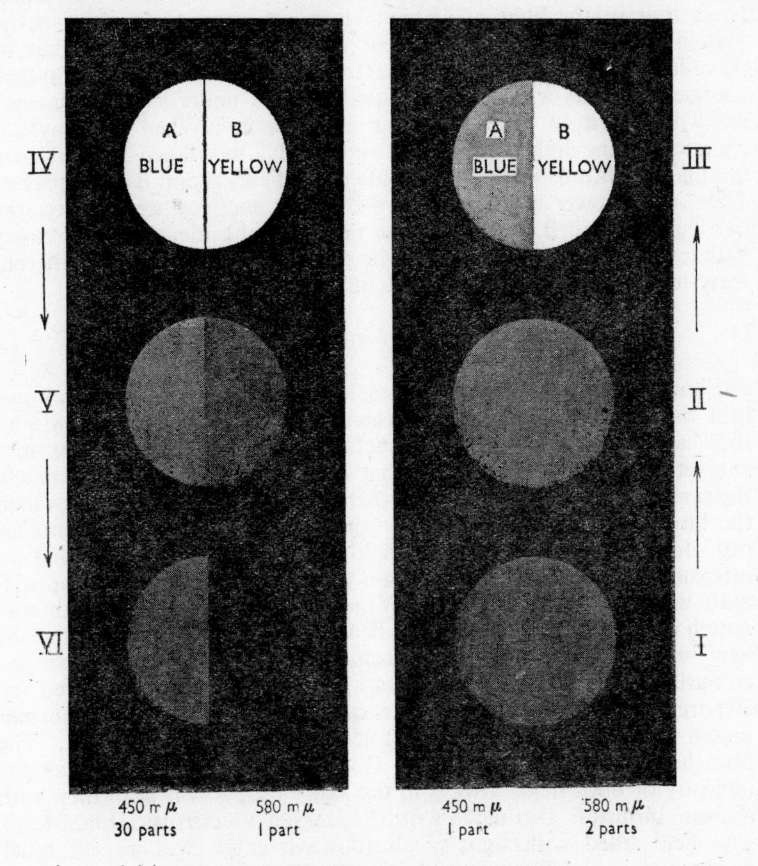

Fig. 34. The Purkinje Phenomenon.
Schematic representation. Explanation in text.

match can be achieved by suitably adjusting the intensities. The two half-fields then appear quite identical, forming one single circular field (Fig. 34, II).

If when such a photometric match is achieved the *physical energies* of the two kinds of lights are measured, it will be found that they are not equal. The physical intensity of the light of 580mμ will be then about twice that of the light of 450mμ. It is clear that such photometric matching and energy measurement can be repeated for any pair of wave-lengths. It is thus possible to determine the relative physical energies of lights which appear equally bright under such conditions; we will return to this important point later. When the physical energies of the lights are raised sufficiently, we return to the more familiar conditions where the colours of the fields A and B are apparent. Then, in whatever way the ratio of the light energies are adjusted, the two fields A and B cannot ever be made to look identical—extremely high intensities being excluded. The eye then gives to lights of different wave-lengths, responses which are qualitatively different.

THE PURKINJE PHENOMENON

Now, although, at high intensities, the two half-fields A and B always look differently coloured, one of them blue, and the other yellow, and thus cannot give a perfect photometric match, the physical intensities can yet be chosen in such a way that A and B appear of approximately the same brightness. At any rate, there is a ratio of intensities for which the blue looks appreciably darker than the yellow field, and another ratio for which it is the yellow field which looks darker, so that an intermediate intensity can be chosen which corresponds to an approximate brightness match (Fig. 34, IV). Even though the new brightness match is not very accurate, it will be found without any doubt that the new intensity ratio is different from the ratio mentioned above for colourless vision at low intensities. The new match is achieved for 30 parts of light of 450mμ and 1 part of light of 580mμ, while the former match was obtained with 1 part of 450mμ and 2 parts of 580mμ. The ratio has thus changed from 2 to 1/30. As a result, if we reduce the intensity of both fields always in the same proportion until they both appear colourless, the match will be completely destroyed (Fig. 34, V). The field filled with light of short wave-length will appear much brighter, since it will now send to the eye 60 times as much radiation as is needed, according to the preceding experiment, in order to match the field filled with light of longer wave-length. And if the intensities are still further reduced, the latter field may become completely invisible, while the field of 450mμ will still remain as a greyish patch (Fig. 34, VI).

It would, of course, also have been possible to increase in an equal ratio, say, by a factor of 10,000, the intensity of each field after the two fields had been matched (Fig. 34, II) at low brightnesses. Then the blue would have appeared darker than the yellow field (Fig. 34, III) since the physical intensity would have been 60 times smaller than that needed for a brightness match at high intensities.

The phenomenon just described can be observed in natural conditions by watching at sunset, and after sunset, the changing appearances of objects such as coloured flowers, materials or paper. As the sun is sinking behind the horizon, the intensity of the illumination it produces on the earth decreases progressively, and the amounts of light reflected by, say, blue and red flowers, decrease simultaneously in the same ratio, since the amounts of coloured light they reflect are in each case proportional to the amount of white light they receive, directly or indirectly, from the sun (possible changes in the spectral composition of the light from the sun being disregarded). Blue flowers reflect predominantly radiation of short wave-length; red flowers, of long wave-length. Suppose they both look about equally bright in daylight; as the illumination slowly decreases, their colours become less and less noticeable and the red flowers get to look darker and darker compared to the blue ones. Eventually, when night has almost come, the red flowers look black, or become invisible, and the blue flowers alone remain visible as greyish patches (1).

It is in such a form that the phenomenon was first described by Purkinje in 1825, and it bears his name (2). The Purkinje phenomenon is of considerable theoretical importance, and it has also an obvious practical importance in visual photometry: care must be taken to make all matches at intensities well outside the transition range in which the phenomenon takes place.

THE DUPLICITY THEORY

The Purkinje phenomenon, and generally the fact that day vision is coloured and sharp, while night vision is colourless and blurred, suggest that there are two different systems of photo-receptors in the retina, one for night vision and one for day vision. In 1866 the anatomist Max Schultze, who had studied the retina of many animals and of man, formulated the theory which is now known as the Duplicity Theory of Vision (3). Schultze found for instance that the retina of day birds, such as the hen, contains a great majority of cones, while night birds, such as the owl, have a retina composed mostly of rods (a number of his drawings are reproduced in Plates II and III). On the basis of thorough investigations, he concluded that the cones are the receptors for day vision and the rods for night vision, and that this is also the case in the human retina, which contains a large number of both cones and rods.

This theory of rods and cones is now well established, after having given rise to many discussions. There are many variations in the structure of rods and cones in different eyes, and even in one and the same eye, so that some cones look rather like rods. The objection is therefore sometimes made that the distinction between rods and cones is an arbitrary one. To this it may first be answered that the assumption that there are two different classes of photo-receptors does not preclude the existence of wide variations between the individual members of each class, so that some members of the one class may happen to have properties similar to those of some members of the other class—they may, for instance, be both very long and thin. On the anatomical side, however, the main answer comes from the distribution of rods and cones in and near the *fovea centralis* of the human eye, as shown in the figures of the preceding chapter. It is clear from these figures that there is one population of receptors, the cones, which are very slender in the centre of the fovea, and become progressively thicker as one goes out towards the periphery. At a certain distance from the centre, one isolated rod appears, very thin among the fat cones; then several more rods appear; the number of rods goes on increasing until, farther out in the periphery of the retina, the big cones are isolated like towers among a dense crowd of rods. Thus, there is a clear discontinuity between the population of rods and the population of cones. To say that rods and cones are extremes of one and the same population is to disregard this. The fact that the cones at the very centre of the fovea resemble rods is no proof that the anatomical distinction between rods and cones is artificial. And even this resemblance seems to be only a superficial one, for Schultze, for instance, states that structurally these foveal elements are, indubitably, cones (see Plate I).

EXPERIMENTS ON THE SENSITIVITY OF DIFFERENT PARTS OF THE RETINA

These anatomical data suggest more precise experiments connected with the preceding ones. In order to test the Duplicity Theory, separate experiments must be made in retinal regions containing cones only, and in regions containing rods and cones. In the preceding experiments a large visual field was used and the subject was allowed to use his eyes as he pleased. It is therefore likely that different parts of his retina were then being used under different conditions. Now we must explore the various parts of the retina using a test field of such a small size that the area covered by its image in any part of the retina may be considered as having a fairly homogeneous structure. Moreover the position of this field on the retina must be accurately known and controlled. This can be achieved by using a fixation point, as will now be explained.

When, under ordinary conditions of daylight, we look at some detail of an object which attracts our attention, our eyes move by a reflex action into such a position that the image of this particular detail falls on to a point in the centre of the *fovea centralis* of our retina, the region where vision of details is most accurate in daylight. Now it is clear that if the head is kept immobile, the position of the eye, and of the retina, *while we look steadily at one point*, will be fixed in space, since the eyeball then cannot rotate round its visual axis. The image

Fig 35.

of the point of fixation is thus maintained on a point of the fovea—with an accuracy of a few minutes of arc in visual angle (4)—and the images of all surrounding objects fall on to the retina in positions which are accurately defined in terms of the position of the objects in space. (In this connection, it must be borne in mind, however, that it is hard to keep accurate fixation for more than a second or two, for, normally, the eye moves in jerks from one position to another every tenth or fifth of a second.) For instance, if the reader, keeping his head steady, looks at the star printed in Fig. 35 with his right eye,

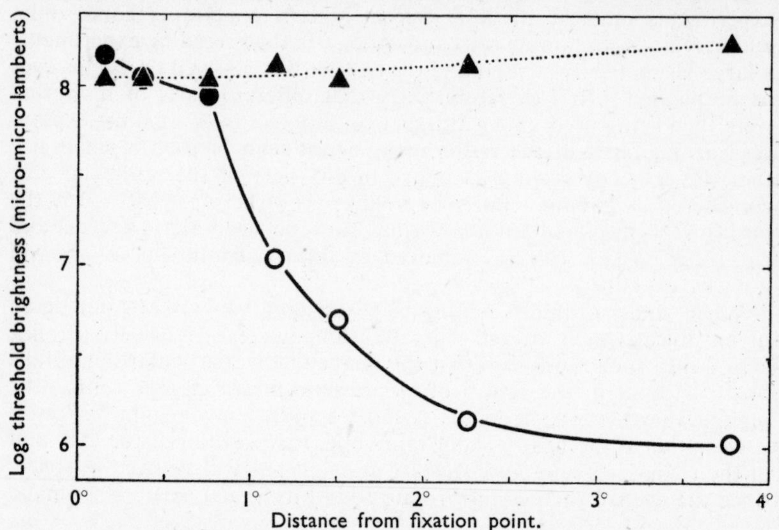

Fig. 36. Threshold values for extreme blue (small circles) and extreme red light (triangles) in various parts of the retina, in and near the fovea.
Explanation in text. The full circles and triangles correspond to coloured vision; the open circles, to colourless vision. See note (7).
The diameter of the test field subtends 10′ at the eye.
(From Pirenne (5), *Nature*, **154**, 741, 1944.)

while shutting the other eye, the image of this asterisk falls on to his fovea, and the image of the small white circle on the left falls laterally to the fovea on the temporal side. At a distance of 1.4 metre from the star, the angle Star—Eye—Circle is about 1.5 degrees and the image of the test field, whose diameter then subtends an angle of 10′ at the eye, covers on the retina an area of 0.05 mm. in diameter and is situated 0·5 mm. from the centre of the fovea—this is readily calculated on the basis given in Chapter I under "Linear Perspective". The same principle was used in the experiment on the blind spot of Chapter I.

It is clear that the above can be readily adapted to conditions of night vision, if the asterisk is replaced by a small source of light which is just bright enough to be clearly seen when the subject looks straight at it. A red point is generally used for reasons which will presently be apparent. The white circle is now replaced by a test field constituted

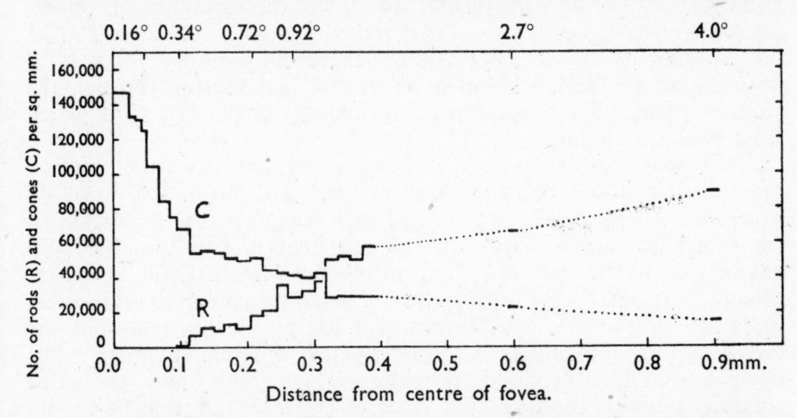

Fig. 37. Distribution of rods and cones in the centre of a human retina. The distances in mm. are uncorrected for shrinkage of the preparation (multiply by 1.31 to obtain the real distances). The corresponding distances in perimetric degrees have been calculated by Østerberg. On the basis given in Chapter I, however, somewhat larger angular values are obtained. Perfect correspondence between this and Fig. 36, of course, cannot be assumed, since they refer to different eyes. (Replotted from the data of Østerberg (6) corresponding to Fig. 28.)

of, say, a piece of opal glass which is limited by a circular diaphragm and which can be illuminated from behind. The wave-length of the light and its intensity can be altered at will using a suitable apparatus. The duration of exposure of the light can also be altered; it is generally presented in flashes lasting for a fraction of a second. Among the reasons for such a choice is the fact that it is not easy to keep fixation for any length of time. The test field can be placed in any position relative to the red fixation point. The experiment takes place in the following way: the subject looks at the fixation point; the light is flashed on to the test field and the subject reports whether he has seen it or not; he then lets his eye wander away and relax, and gets ready for a new flash.

Fig. 36 shows the results of experiments made in this way on the right eye of a dark-adapted subject (5). Light from the extreme blue end and light from the extreme red end of the visible spectrum was used. The duration of the flash was 0·04 of a second. The physical intensity of light necessary in order that the subject can just see the light, is known as the *threshold* intensity. The lower the threshold, therefore, the higher is the sensitivity of the retina to light. The first aim of the experiments was to determine the threshold intensity, for various positions of the test field on a horizontal line passing through the fixation point. The appearance and colour of the test field, when seen, was also noted.

The abscissa of Fig. 36 gives, in degrees, the angle (Fixation point)—Eye—(Test field). The ordinate gives the logarithm of the threshold intensity. For example, at an angle of 1·5 degrees, the logarithm of the threshold intensity for extreme red light is 8·0; the threshold intensity is 100,000,000 $\mu\mu$l; (the micro-micro-lambert, $\mu\mu$l, is a convenient, very small, unit of brightness. Brightnesses expressed in these units are proportional to the physical energy of the light, but the factor of proportionality is different for different lights.). The logarithm of the threshold for extreme blue light under the same conditions is 6·7; the threshold value is 5,000,000 $\mu\mu$l, that is, twenty times less than the value for red light. At small angles, however, the figure shows that the threshold values for red and blue are very close to one another. This is due to the particular choice of brightness units, but the fundamental difference between the centre and periphery is of course independent of units. For blue light, the threshold decreases slightly as the angular distance between test field and fixation point increases from 0·15 to 0·75 degrees. Then it drops suddenly and at 3.75 degrees it is about 2 logarithmic units lower than near the centre of the fovea. At angles up to 0·75 degrees, the subject reported that the field, when seen at all, appeared of a deep violet or blue colour; at the higher angles it always appeared colourless. For red light the threshold value changes little with the angle, being slightly higher at higher angles. When it was seen, the test field always appeared red. At an angle of 7·5 degrees, however, the light appeared orange, and farther out it appeared first yellow and then colourless.

These findings must now be compared with anatomical data. Fig. 37 gives the distribution of rods and cones in the central part of a human retina. The foveal centre contains only cones, the first rods appearing at an angle of about 0·4 degree. The number of rods per unit area

1. PERIPHERY 2. NEAR YELLOW SPOT 3. NEARER TO YELLOW SPOT 4. EDGE OF YELLOW SPOT

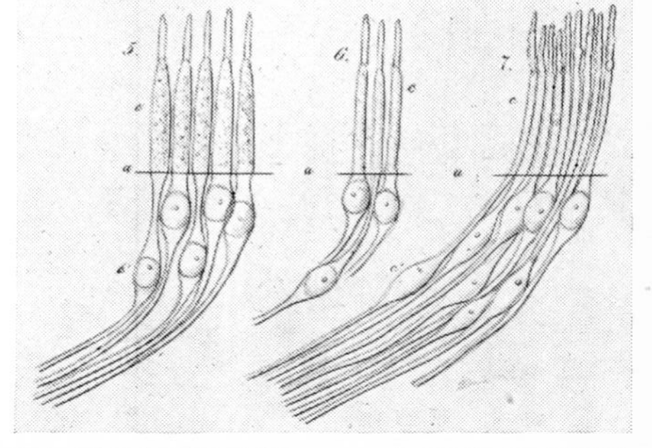

5, 6. IN YELLOW SPOT 7. EDGE OF FOVEA

PLATE I

RODS AND CONES WITH THEIR NERVOUS ENDINGS IN THE HUMAN RETINA

The structure of the segments of the cones changes progressively from the periphery to the fovea, but their nervous endings remain different from those of the rods.

It will be noted how in central regions the nervous fibres of the cones run obliquely toward the ora serrata. The complete length of the fibres which are shown in part in Figs. 5, 6, & 7, is as much as six times the length of the fibres in Fig. 4.

The outer segments of the cones are crumpled by the fixative used. The rods are drawn as they appear in the fresh state.

Osmic acid preparation. Magnification 300.

From Schultze, *Arch. mikr. Anat.* **2**, 175, 1866.

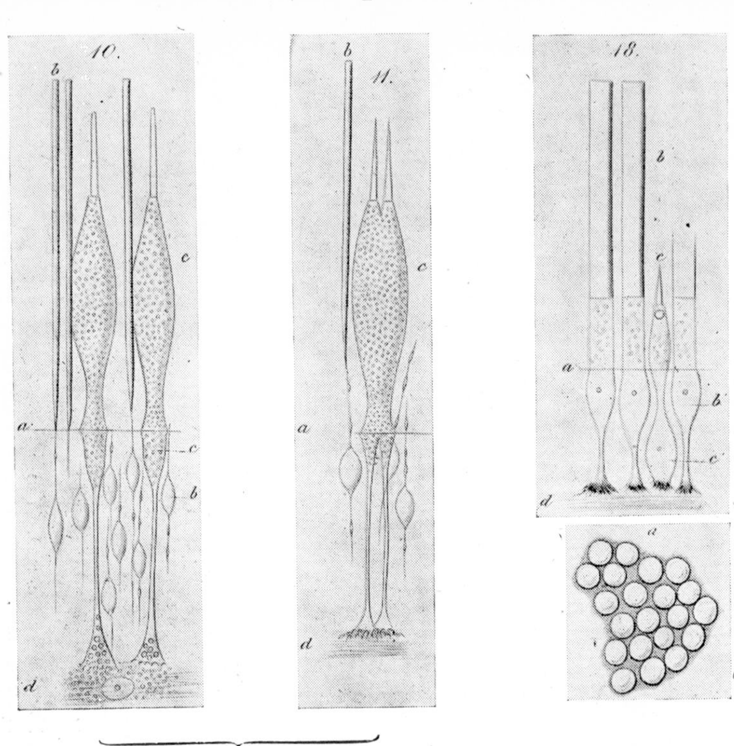

PLATE II

PARTS OF THE RETINA OF VARIOUS ANIMALS

Note the " double cone " in the case of the perch (*Perca fluviatilis*) and the large size of the rods of the frog (*Rana temporaria*). The retinae of the cat and of the dog contain both rods and cones and in this respect resemble the periphery of the human retina. The retina of the bat (*Vespertilio* sp.) contains rods only.

The lower drawings in the case of the frog, cat and bat give an endwise view of the disposition of the photo-receptors, as shown in Fig. 25 for the human retina.

The retinal sections were made after fixation with osmic or chromic acid.

Magnification 400 to 500.

From Schultze, *Arch. mikr. Anat.* **2**, 175, 1866.

3

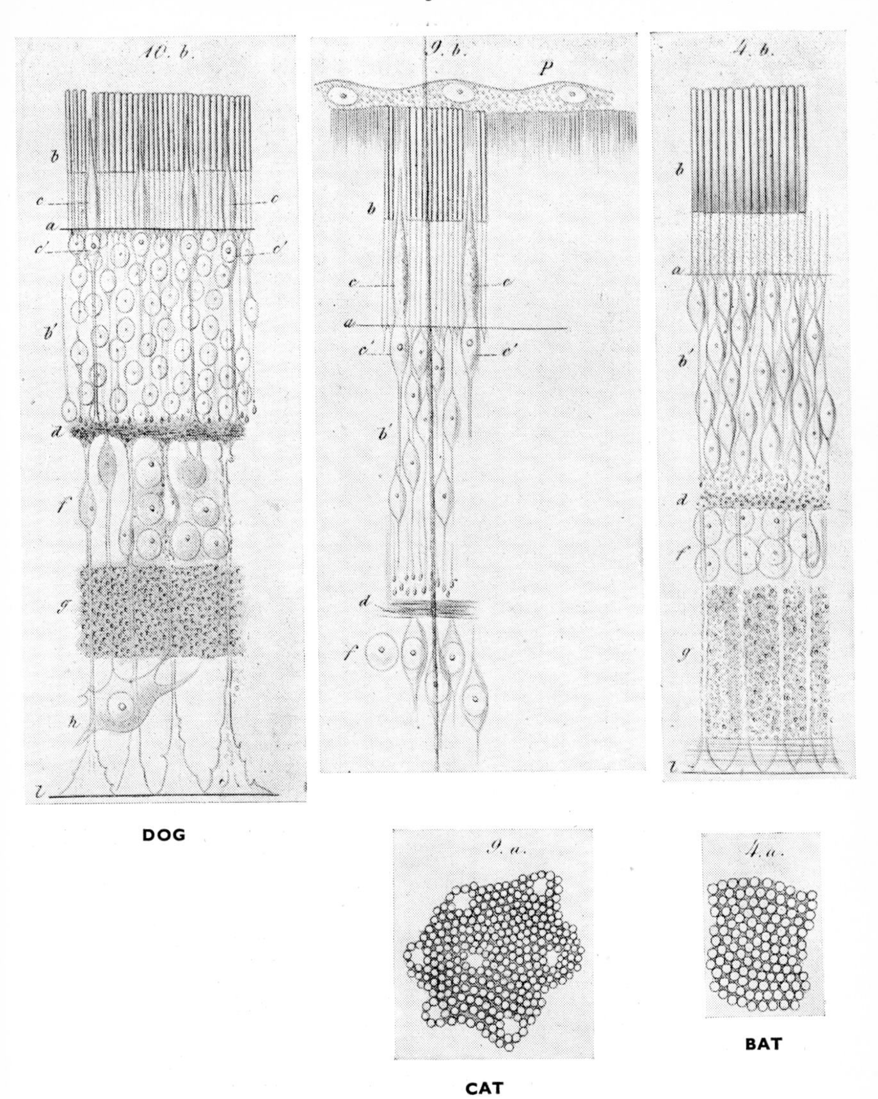

PLATE III

RODS AND CONES OF VARIOUS BIRDS AND OF A LIZARD

The cones of birds and lizards contain coloured or colourless fat globules. The rods appear colourless under the microscope because their visual purple has been bleached by the microscope light.

Pigeon. On the left is a magnified view of a lateral part of the retina, which looks reddish, and which serves for vision forward. The drawing on the right corresponds to the other retinal regions. The colourless circles are rods; the yellow and red circles are cones. Among the yellow cones, all represented here by the same tint, some are, in fact, orange in colour. These darker cones are more numerous in the reddish parts of the retina.

The middle drawing is a lateral view of four cones and one rod of the reddish region.

Crow (*Corvus Corone*). Surface views of the retina with the black pigment attached to it. The ends of the rods (white circles) and cones (red and yellow circles) pass through the pigment layer.

The fovea centralis of the crow contains rods—much thinner than the peripheral rods—as well as yellow and red cones.

Falcon (*Falco buteo*). Same preparation as for the crow.

The retina has two foveae, which contain thin yellow cones only.

At the edge of the fovea, thin rods appear among the yellow cones. The periphery contains thick rods, yellow cones and red cones.

Young Owl (probably *Strix aluco*). The long rods here tend to hide the cones. The top drawing is a surface view of the rods, in between which dark spaces indicate the position of the cones. In the lower drawing, the outer limbs of the rods have been broken away, the yellow globules of the cones coming then into evidence. The drawing on the right in the middle of the plate gives a lateral view of the rods and of the cones. The cones contain pale yellow globules.

Owl (*Strix noctua*). The very long rods hide the cones in the surface view of the retina. The drawing on the left in the middle of the plate gives a lateral view of the rods and cones, the former being extremely long.

Lizard (*Lacerta viridis*). Surface and lateral view of the cones.
The white elements are not rods, but cones containing colourless globules.

Retinae in the fresh natural state, except for the lateral view of the owl retina.
Magnification 300 to 400.

Redrawn after Schultze, *Arch. mikr. Anat.* **2**, 175, 1866.

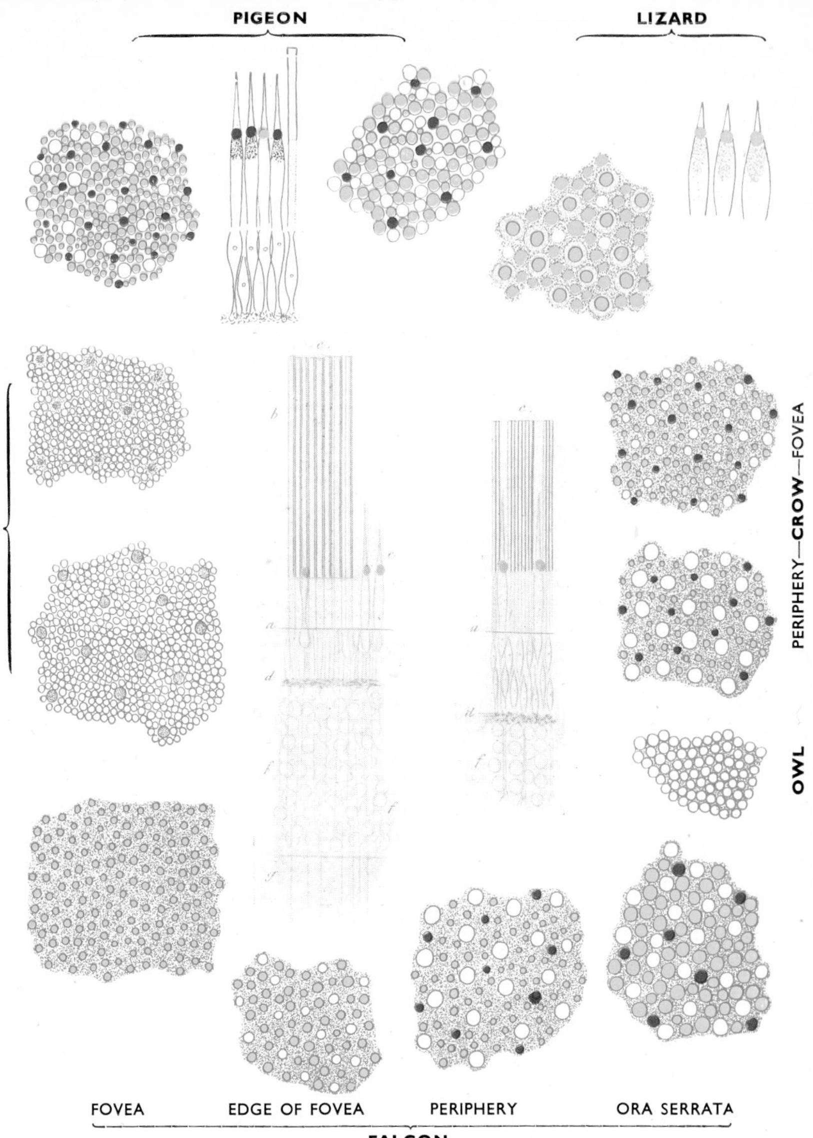
PIGEON
LIZARD
YOUNG OWL
PERIPHERY—CROW—FOVEA
OWL
FOVEA
EDGE OF FOVEA
PERIPHERY
ORA SERRATA
FALCON

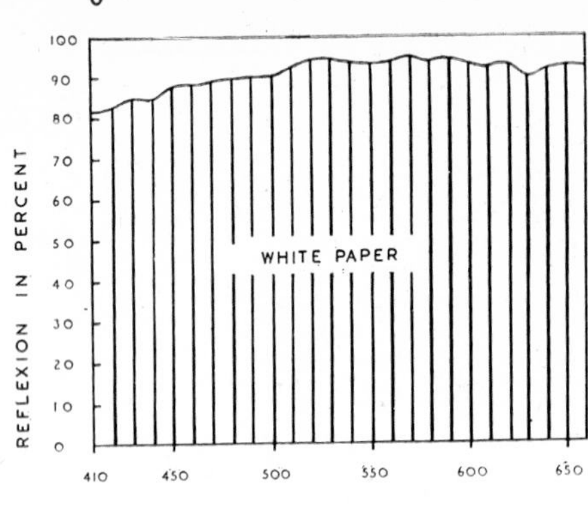

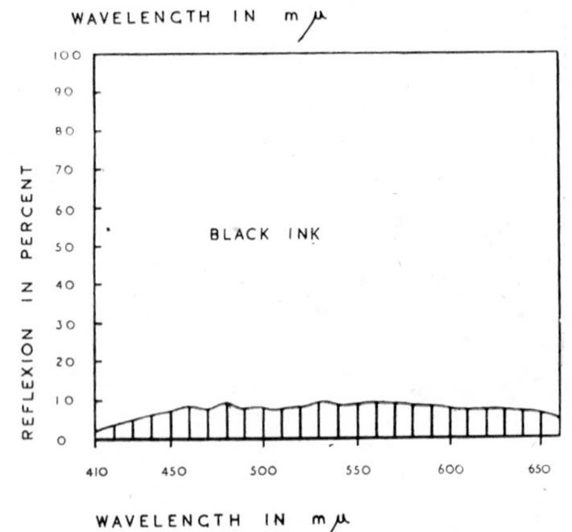

Plate IV. Spectral reflexion curves of white paper, of paper covered with black ink, with yellow ink, with blue ink, and with blue ink superimposed on yellow ink, which gives a dark green.

Note that the white paper reflects less than 100 per cent. of the light incident upon it, while the black paper reflects a noticeable amount of light—about 8 per cent.

The yellow and blue inks both present very broad regions of high reflexion.

The dark green obtained by superimposing blue on yellow ink reflects only the light reflected by both blue and yellow. At 520 mμ, for instance, yellow reflects 0.81, blue 0.41, and blue-on-yellow reflects 0.34 : the latter is approximately equal to (0.81 $\times$ 0.41). Such "subtractive mixtures" of pigments thus produce results entirely different from those of additive mixtures of lights. The physiology of vision deals *directly* only with the mixtures of *lights*.

(The above reflexion curves were kindly measured by Messrs. Imperial Chemical Industries, Dyestuff Division.)

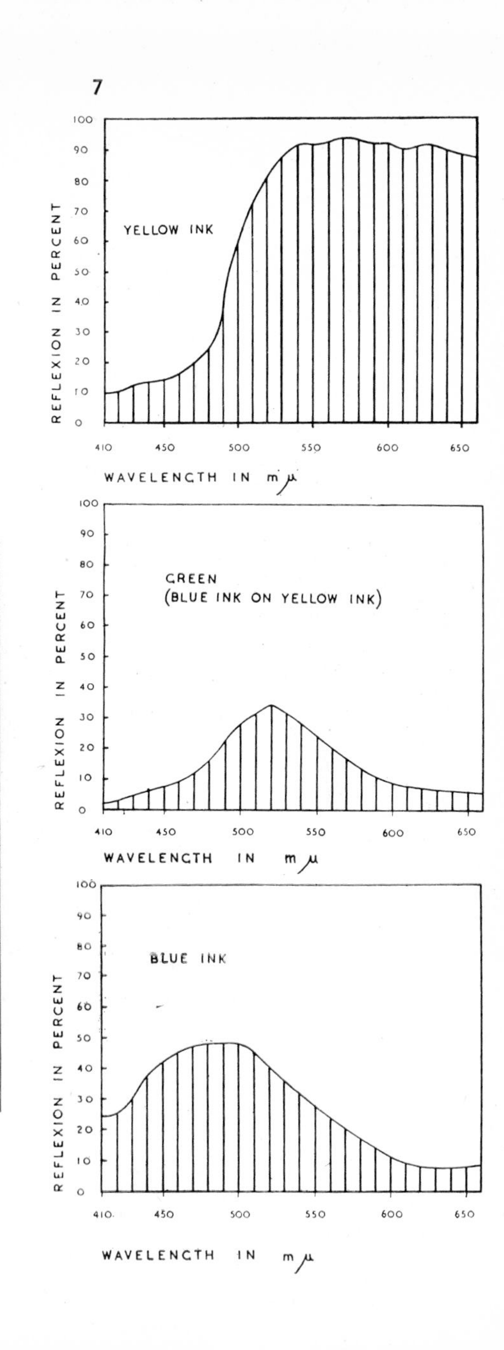
YELLOW INK
REFLEXION IN PERCENT
WAVELENGTH IN mμ
GREEN
(BLUE INK ON YELLOW INK)
REFLEXION IN PERCENT
WAVELENGTH IN mμ
BLUE INK
REFLEXION IN PERCENT
WAVELENGTH IN mμ

goes on increasing while the number of cones decreases, the two numbers being equal at an angle of about 1 degree. Comparison of Figs 36 and 37 clearly shows that, for blue light, the threshold is high and the light is seen coloured in the rod-free area, while the threshold is much lower and the light appears colourless in the area where the rods are considerably more numerous than the cones, that is, at angles larger than 2 degrees. In the intermediate region, the passage from coloured to colourless vision occurs only at an angle where the rods are fairly numerous, as might have been expected. For red light, the presence or absence of rods has little influence on the value of the threshold or on the colour of the light in the region studied here.

Thus the region of the retina containing cones only has properties different from those of rod-containing regions; when monochromatic light falling within the rod-free area is seen at all, it is seen as coloured. (7) Normal night vision is in general colourless because the central rod-free area does not function at very low intensities, except for extreme red light; the rods, in the periphery, then as a rule remain the only receptors to be excited (8).

The experiments just discussed refer only to a small region of the retina close to the fovea; it is interesting to study also the peripheral retina, since, as has been seen, lateral vision can extend to high angles. Fig. 38 shows the sensitivity of parts of the dark-adapted retina chosen along a horizontal meridian, including very peripheral regions. The results refer to a right eye. The test field is circular and its diameter subtends 3 degrees at the eye, its retinal image thus having an area equal to 324 times that of the field used in the experiments of Fig. 36. The time of exposure was 0.2 second instead of 0.04 second. The experimental arrangement is shown diagrammatically in Fig. 39. The test field and the fixation point are both placed on a horizontal circle having its centre at the eye; their relative position, and thus the *perimetric angle* α, can be altered at will. "Nasal," in Figs. 38 and 39, means that the test field is placed in the same position relative to the fixation point as the nose is to the eye. "Temporal" means the opposite side. The brightness units are the same as those of Fig. 36. As the size of the field and the time of exposure are different, the results in terms of brightness are also different. For an angle of 0 degree—that is, when the centre of the test field coincides with the fixation point—the image of the test field falls on the fovea; but, on account of its size, it also covers a region containing many rods, and the results are not very well defined physiologically. At high angles α—that is, in very peripheral regions

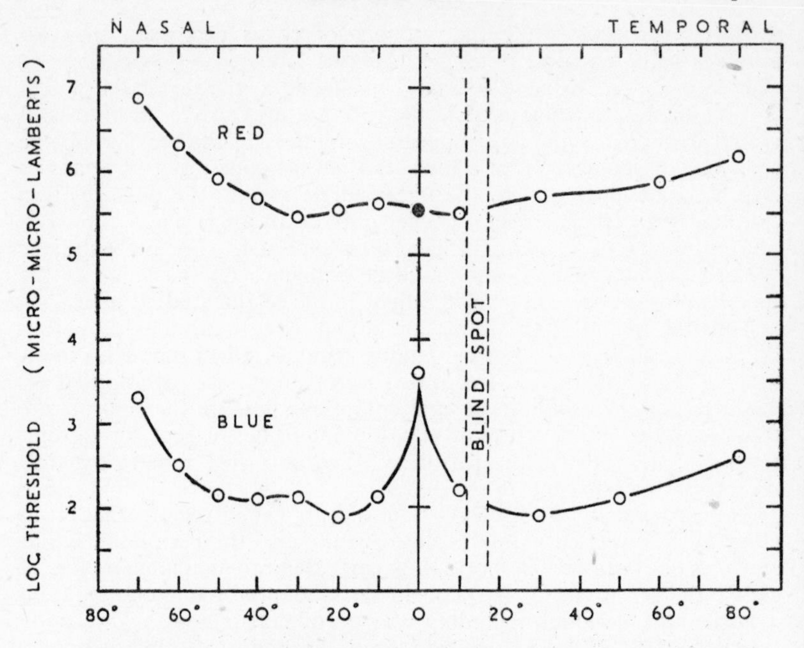

Fig. 38. Threshold values of a right eye for red and blue light.
Test field 3° in diameter. Explanation in text. Cf. Fig. 29.
(Unpublished measurements.)

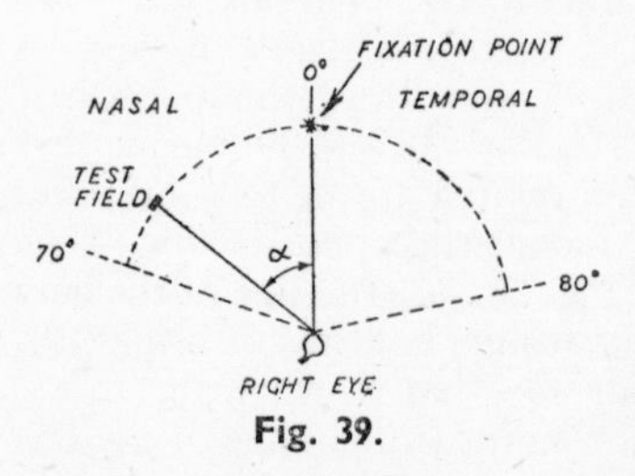

Fig. 39.

of the retina—many factors, such as the obliquity of the plane of the pupil relative to the incoming rays, must be expected to affect the threshold values, besides the sensivity of the retina itself.

The results again show the contrast between the results obtained using blue light and red light, with regard to the local variation of retinal sensivity. Unlike the case of blue, there is little change in the threshold value for red light in the central part of the retina. For blue light, to which the rods are very sensitive, there is a broad region of high sensitivity at angles α around 20 or 30 degrees. This position corresponds to an area of high density of rods in the retina, as has been seen in Fig. 29 of the preceding chapter. The test field always appeared colourless, except for red light at an angle of 0 degree (i.e. in direct vision), when the field appeared of a deep red colour.

Consideration of Figs. 36 and 38 shows that a source of blue light may be so faint that it can just be seen when its image falls on a peripheral part of the retina, while it remains unseen when it falls in the foveal region. If the gaze is directed straight at such a light, the light disappears, although it is visible when looked at peripherally. The same applies, at least to some extent, to other physical lights, with the important exception of those of the red end of the spectrum. In the case of red light, as shown especially by Fig. 36, the fovea is generally slightly more sensitive than the periphery (7). A dim red point source is thus most convenient as a fixation point in experiments made using the dark-adapted eye. For, when fixation is inaccurate, the point tends to become less visible—while if a blue fixation point were used, its visibility would then increase.

BIBLIOGRAPHY AND NOTES

(1) Under these circumstances, however, white flowers would appear brighter than blue ones, because white flowers reflect the radiations reflected by the blue, *plus* all the other radiations of the visible spectrum. These matters are discussed in Chapter XI, on Newton's doctrine of colour.

(2) PURKINJE, J. E. (1825). *Zur Physiologie der Sinne*, vol. ii, p. 109, Berlin.

(3) SCHULTZE, M. (1866). "Zur Anatomie und Physiologie der Retina," *Arch. mikr. Anat.*, **2,** 175.

It is curious to note that, notwithstanding Schultze's renown in the scientific world, the ideas he expressed in this masterly paper at first attracted little attention.

(4) ADLER, F. H., and FLIEGELMAN, M. (1934). *Arch. Ophthalm.*, **12,** 475.

(5) PIRENNE, M. H. (1944). "Rods and Cones, and Thomas Young's Theory of Colour Vision," *Nature*, **154,** 741.

(6) ØSTERBERG, G. (1935). "Topography of the Layer of Rods and Cones in the Human Retina," *Acta Ophthalm.*, Suppl. 6.
(7) Certain peculiarities of colour-vision are observed when small foveal fields are used. See Chapter XIII, on Normal Colour Vision. Although very small, the fovea has properties which vary greatly from point to point. For instance, in its very centre, there is a sharp maximum of sensitivity for red and a sharp minimum for blue spectral light—not shown in Fig. 36. See W. S. Stiles in the Proceedings of the International Conference on Colour Vision held in Cambridge in 1947.
(8) HECHT, S. (1937). "Rods, Cones, and the Chemical Basis of Vision," *Physiol. Rev.*, **17**, 239.
A modern review.

Chapter IV

SPECTRAL SENSITIVITY CURVES

PHYSICAL STIMULI PRODUCING THE SAME PHYSIOLOGICAL EFFECT

In the preceding chapter, it was explained that, at very low intensities, perfect photometric matches between different monochromatic lights can be obtained. As was said in connexion with Fig. 34, II, of Chapter III, it is possible to measure the physical energies of lights which appear identical to the eye under such conditions. Keeping the light in one of the half fields, *A*, unchanged in all respects throughout the experiments, it is possible to fill the other half field, *B*, in turn with lights of other wave-lengths of the spectrum, and to obtain a match for each of them. If the different physical energies of the light so used in field *B* are then plotted against their wave-length, a curve is obtained. This curve gives the relative amounts of light which are needed in order to produce *the same physiological effect* on the eye—that is, the same effect as that produced by the light of the half field *A*, which serves as a constant standard of reference.

DEFINITION OF SENSITIVITY

Instead of the energy E of the light in half field B, its reciprocal $\frac{1}{E}$ can be plotted against the wave-length. The value $\frac{1}{E}$ is often referred to as the sensitivity of the eye to the corresponding light, or as the luminosity, visibility or effectiveness of the light. These are but names, however. The actual meaning of $\frac{1}{E}$ is that given above. In particular, these sensitivity curves do *not* represent the magnitude of the reaction produced in the organism by equal amounts of light of different wave-length, and to consider they do so leads to grave error and confusion. Other spectral sensitivity curves corresponding to other physiological effects can be obtained.

ROD AND CONE SENSITIVITY CURVES

The energy required to produce threshold stimulation, for instance, can be measured in the different parts of the spectrum. Sensitivity curves of this kind are reproduced in Fig. 40. The two full lines are drawn through threshold measurements made in a way similar to those of the preceding chapter. One of the curves refers to cones at the fovea; the other, to the periphery and to rod vision. The broken line represents

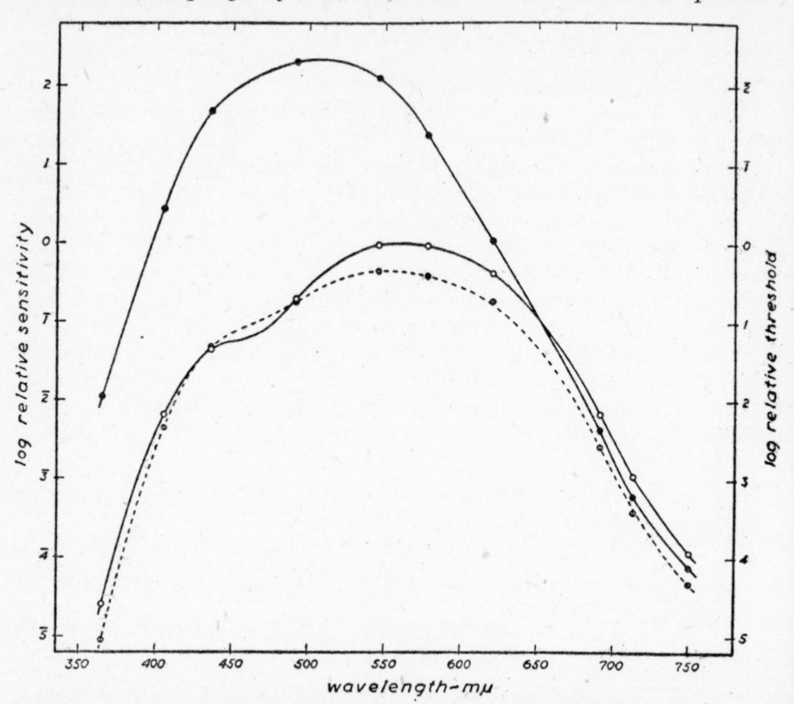

Fig. 40. Spectral sensitivities (1/threshold E) of dark-adapted elements of the human eye.

Rods, 8° above the fovea (black circles, full line). Foveal cones (open circles, full line). Peripheral cones, 8° above fovea (broken line). Test field 1° in diameter, exposed for durat ons of 0.04 sec. All sensitivities are expressed relative to the maximum sensitivity of the fovea.
(From Wald (1), *Science*, **101**, 653, 1945.)

the sensitivity curve of cones in the periphery of the retina, obtained using a special method. The rod curve and the cone curves are very similar for wave-lengths above 650mμ, that is, in the red end of the spectrum. They differ widely in the rest of the spectrum, both with regard to their position on the sensitivity scale and to the position of their maxima. The rods are most sensitive to light of wave-length 510mμ while the cones are most sensitive to light of about 560mμ.

Such sensitivity curves have a fundamental physiological importance and summarize a considerable amount of information. The shape of the sensitivity curve obtained using the photometric matching method of Fig. 34, II, is practically the same as that of the rod curve of Fig. 40. A sensitivity curve corresponding to Fig. 34, IV, can be obtained at high intensities although, as has been seen, the difference of colour between the half fields *A* and *B* then leads to results having a much less definite meaning than the case of Fig. 34, II. The curve obtained in this way (Fig. 43) has a shape similar to that of the cone curves in Fig. 40. Accordingly many of the facts of the preceding chapter, including the Purkinje phenomenon, can be derived in detail from a consideration of such sensitivity curves. For instance, it can be seen that the sensitivity of the foveal cones to extreme red is slightly higher than the sensitivity of the rods, while the latter are relatively much more sensitive to light of shorter wave-length. They are, for example, about a thousand times more sensitive to light of 450mμ. It will be noted that since logarithm of $\frac{1}{E}$ is equal to minus logarithm of E, such curves as those of Fig. 40, in which the sensitivity is plotted on a logarithmic scale, give immediately the threshold energy values simply by changing the sign of the ordinate.

VISUAL PURPLE

The outer segments of the rods of the retina contain a substance called *visual purple*. This substance, as its name indicates, is purple or pink in colour, and has the property of being bleached by light. By chemical operations, visual purple, which has many of the properties of a protein, can be extracted from, e.g., frog retinae, purified, and studied *in vitro*. The best known of its properties is its spectral absorption curve. This curve gives for each wave-length the fraction of the incident light which is absorbed by a given layer of visual purple solution.

It is now well established that when light acts upon the rod visual system, it is first absorbed by the visual purple contained in the rods. It bleaches the visual purple, and the subsequent physico-chemical reactions lead to the stimulation of the nervous endings of the rod cells, and eventually to stimulation of fibres of the optic nerve. What matters then is how much visual purple is bleached by light, not what kind or what amount of light is used to cause this result. This explains why there is no discrimination of wave-length as such in rod vision.

The amount of visual purple bleached is proportional to the amount of light (estimated in quanta, see Chapter VII) which is absorbed by the visual purple. If therefore visual purple in the rods absorbs for 500mμ a fraction of the incident light ten times that for light of 590mμ,

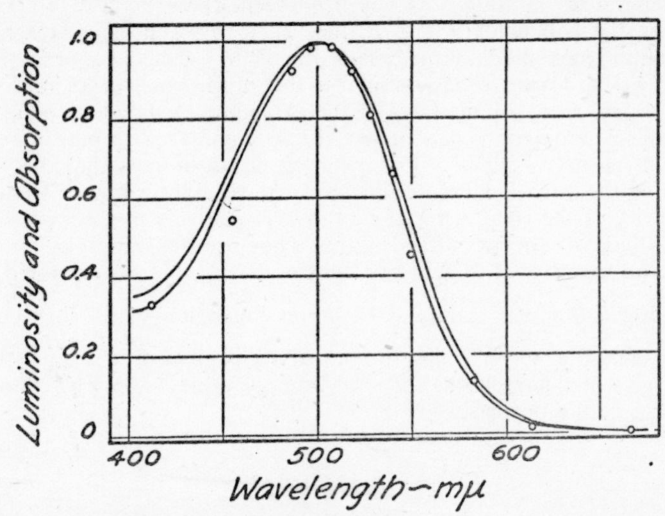

Fig. 41. Comparison of the rod visibility curve with the spectral absorption of visual purple.

The circles represent the visibility curve corrected for quantum effectiveness and transmission by the ocular media. This curve is proportional to : 1/(number of $h\nu$ striking the retina). The full lines represent absorption spectra of visual purple; the upper curve corresponds to 20 per cent. maximum absorption and the lower one to 5 per cent. maximum absorption. These curves are proportional to: (n° of $h\nu$ absorbed)/(n° of $h\nu$ incident). The ordinates of all curves have been made equal to unity at the maximum, 500 mμ, for ease in comparison.

(From Hecht, Shlaer and Pirenne (2), *J. Gen. Physiol.*, **25**, 819, 1942.)

the amount of light necessary for producing the same physiological effect in the rod system will be ten times less for 500 than for 590mμ, and the retinal sensitivity as defined above, will be ten times higher. The absorption curve of the visual purple in the rods of the dark-adapted eye thus must coincide in shape with the rod sensitivity when the latter is modified to take into account such factors as quantum effectiveness and the transmission of the eye media, which is not the same for all wave-lengths. Fig. 41 shows that this correspondence exists when a concentration of visual purple in the rods corresponding to a maximum absorption of the order 10 per cent. is assumed—the shape of the absorption curve varying with the concentration merely on account of the physical laws of light absorption. (A similar state of affairs may be expected to exist for the cones, or rather for each type of cone, as explained in Chapter XV, but satisfactory experimental results have not yet been obtained.)

SEEING IN THE DARK

In the dark-adapted eye the peripheral parts of the retina are more sensitive to light than the central area, except, as we have seen, when light belonging to the red end of the spectrum is used to the exclusion of any other. The rod-containing periphery of the retina must therefore be used for night-vision. Many people, during " black-out " hours, discovered this fact empirically for themselves, without knowing precisely what was involved. Peripheral vision of this kind necessitates some preliminary training; but it is the only method, apart from the use of artificial instruments, for seeing on very dark nights.

Some animals, such as nocturnal owls, are able to catch their prey in extremely dark surroundings. In this connexion an investigator had put forward the view that owls had a very special kind of visual system, which enabled them to see their prey in absolute darkness. In the complete absence of ordinary visible light, for instance, they would still be able to see a mouse, by the radiation emitted by the mouse itself. Because of its temperature, the body of the mouse emits radiation which belongs, not to the visible, but to the infra-red region of the spectrum. The eye of the owl was supposed to be sensitive to this infra-red radiation emitted by the body of the mouse. That is, the owl would see its prey in the same way as we see a red-hot poker in the dark, the only difference being that the mouse is not red hot, but only " infra-red hot."

This appears to be untenable on theoretical grounds. For the eye of the owl itself is at a temperature of approximately 40°C, as is the body of the mouse. This means that the eye is also " infra-red hot ". The situation is therefore the same as if one tried to obtain a picture of a red-hot poker inside a *camera obscura* which in turn is itself raised to a red-hot temperature. The image of the poker would tend to be washed out in the midst of the diffuse red light emitted by the camera itself and filling it completely (3).

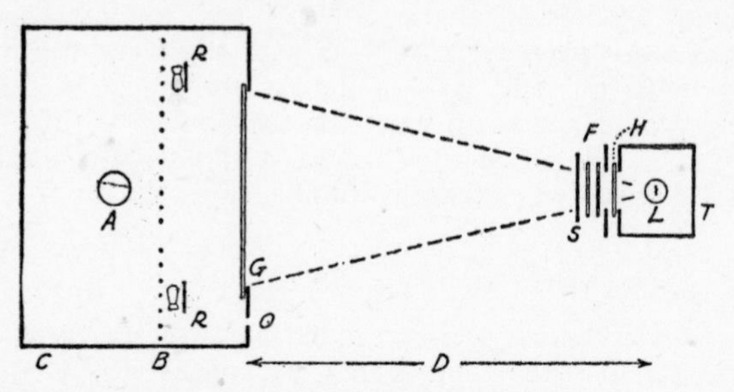

Fig. 42. Measurement of the spectral sensitivity of the owl.

The owl sitting at *A* on a rod in the cage *C* sees the ground glass *G* which is illuminated by light from the lamp *L* after it has passed through various filters *F* for controlling its intensity and spectral composition. Two deep red lamps *R* illuminate the owl so that its bright yellow iris is just adequately visible to the observer whose eye is at *O*.

(From Hecht and Pirenne (4), *J. Gen. Physiol.*, **23**, 709, 1940.)

Experiments were, however, made to test the idea directly (4). The owl was placed in a cage, facing a large screen of ground glass (Fig. 42). Light of varying wave-length and energy could be projected on this screen. When this was done the iris of the owl's eye generally contracted, appearing as a bright yellow rim around the black pupil. Other times the pupil was fully dilated and the iris appeared as a thin, yellow line just visible around the large dark pupil.

The amount of green light (510mμ) needed to obtain a minimal contraction of the iris, that is, a just noticeable thickening of the yellow rim, was determined. This minimal iris contraction was adopted here as the constant physiological effect in relation to which the sensitivity curve is determined.

An attempt was then made to produce an iris contraction using infra-red radiation (of wave-length equal to about 1 micron) instead of green light. The highest energy used was 5,000,000 times as much as the green light energy capable of eliciting a response, but none was observed. The hypothesis that the owl sees its prey by means of the infra-red radiation emitted by the prey must therefore be rejected.

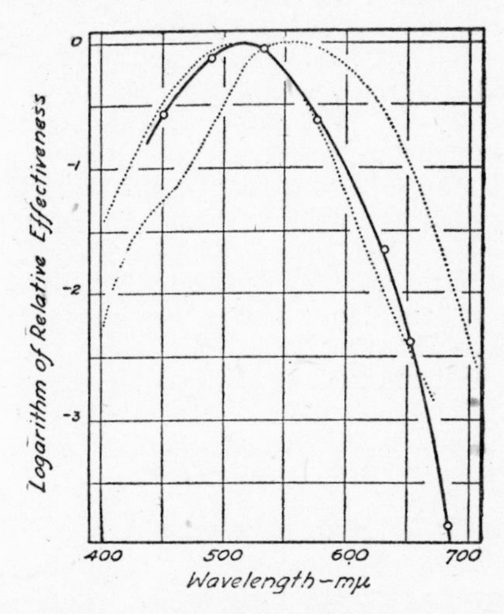

Fig. 43. Spectral sensitivities of the owl and of man.
The points connected by a continuous line are the average data of five series of measurements with the owl. The dotted lines represent the spectral sensitivity curves of the human eye. The one at the left is obtained at very low intensities and represents rod function ; the one at the right is obtained at high intensities and represents cone function. Cf. Fig. 40. The maxima of all curves are arbitrarily set at the same ordinate value.
(From Hecht and Pirenne (4), *J. Gen. Physiol.*, **23**, 709, 1940.)

The whole visibility curve of the owl was obtained by the same technique, i.e. by measuring the relative amounts of luminous energy needed at different wave-lengths in order to obtain a minimal contraction of the iris. As Fig. 43 shows, this curve is the same in shape and position as the curve for human rod vision—within the limits of experimental error. It is quite different from the human cone visibility curve.

This finding agrees with the fact that the owl's retina consists almost exclusively of rods, as is shown in Plate III. Therefore, there is nothing strikingly new about the night visual system of the owl, which is a rod system. Extrapolation of the rod visibility curve towards the infra-red explains why no response could be obtained to the infra-red energy used in the experiment.

The visibility curve so obtained does not give the absolute visual threshold of the owl, which it would be interesting to compare with that of man. Various indirect estimates suggest that the owl's absolute threshold may be ten times lower than our threshold. This would be due mostly to the fact that with the same external brightness the owl could collect more light on his retina, his eye being a camera with a larger aperture than ours. Consequently, a daık night may appeaı to the owl much the same as a night in which the illumination is ten times higher appears to us. The term " complete darkness " is generally used as a relative term, meaning only complete darkness *for us*, not complete absence of light. In this sense it is possible that the owl still sees under conditions which we would describe as " complete darkness," though of course he cannot do so in the complete absence of light.

BIBLIOGRAPHY

(1) WALD, G. (1945). " Human vision and the spectrum," *Science*, **101**, 653–658.

(2) HECHT, S., SHLAER, S., and PIRENNE, M. H. (1942). " Energy, Quanta, and Vision," *J. General Physiology*, **25**, 819–840.

(3) PIRENNE, M. H. (1947). " The thermal radiation inside the eye and the red end of the spectral sensitivity curve," *J. Physiol.* **106**, 25P.

CZERNY, M. (1933). " Grenzen der Messtechnik," *Zs. f. techn. Physik.*, **14**, 436–440.

(4) HECHT, S., and PIRENNE, M. H. (1940). " The Sensibility of the nocturnal long-eared owl in the spectrum," *J. General Physiology*, **23**, 709–717.

Chapter V

THE NERVOUS ACTIVITY PRODUCED IN THE EYE BY THE ACTION OF LIGHT

ELECTRICAL PHENOMENA IN NERVES

It has been known for more than a century that the activity of nerves is accompanied by electrical phenomena. The scale of such phenomena is small; for this reason, our knowledge of them has grown slowly. Progress in this field depended on technical advances which would make it possible to measure very weak and transient electrical currents. Other physico-chemical changes, besides electrical, take place in a nerve when it is thrown into activity. The electrical changes, however, are by far the easiest to study, so that their recording has become the universal method of investigating the manifestation of nervous activity.

Even the electric changes which occur in a single fibre of a nerve can now be recorded. These changes can be more easily interpreted than the changes recorded during the electric activity of a whole nerve, composed as it is of a great number of fibres which may all be active at the same time. The technical difficulties are very much greater, however, and it is only in recent years that they have been surmounted. About twenty years ago the first recordings of single fibre activity were made, the fibres being those connected with such sensory cells as the touch receptors in the skin (1, 2). More recently this was achieved in the case of single fibres connected to visual receptors stimulated by light in the ordinary way (3).

ACTIVITY OF SINGLE NERVE FIBRES

When a nerve fibre is stimulated, local physico-chemical changes take place in it which are propagated rapidly along the fibre. This propagated disturbance can be detected by changes of electrical potential which manifest themselves between active and inactive regions of the fibres. Each part of the fibre surface in turn becomes electronegative relative to the remaining regions. A wave of electronegativity thus travels along the length of the fibre. In the diagrams of Fig. 44, the active electronegative region is shown stippled; as the wave of electronegativity moves to the right of the figure, the region which was previously negative returns to normal, while successive regions to the right of it become temporarily negative. This is shown in the temporal sequence (*a*), (*b*) and (*c*) of the figure. Let us now consider two electrodes, one placed in contact with the fibre at A, an uninjured region,

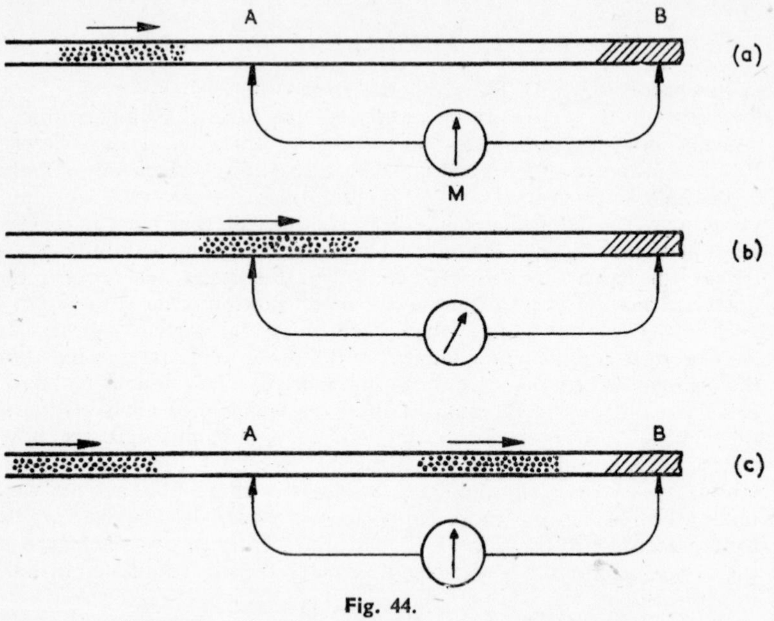

Fig. 44.
Schematic. Not drawn to scale. Explanation in text.

and the other at B, at the cut end of the fibre. The instrument M records the difference of potential between A and B. This difference has a steady value as long as the fibre is inactive. But when it is excited, and a wave of electronegativity reaches the electrode A, the value of the potential difference is momentarily altered as the potential of the region A decreases. The measuring instrument M then records this change (*b*). The wave of electronegativity as a rule moves along the fibre with a velocity of many metres per second, while the length of the wave of electronegativity on the fibre is only a few centimetres, so that the potential change recorded is very transient.

Other waves of negativity generally follow the first: a second wave is shown to the left of Fig. 44 (*c*) before it has reached the electrode A. An excited nerve-fibre thus transmits rapidly along its length successive waves of electronegativity, which are recorded as electrical impulses. Fig. 45 shows schematically the time course of the changes of potential between electrodes A and B. At first the difference of potential is steady (*a*). Then the potential of electrode A changes for a short time (*b*), and returns rapidly to normal (*c*), when the wave of electronegativity has passed beyond the electrode A. When the second wave, shown to the left of diagram (*c*) in Fig. 44, passes over the electrode A, a second impulse is recorded (*d*).

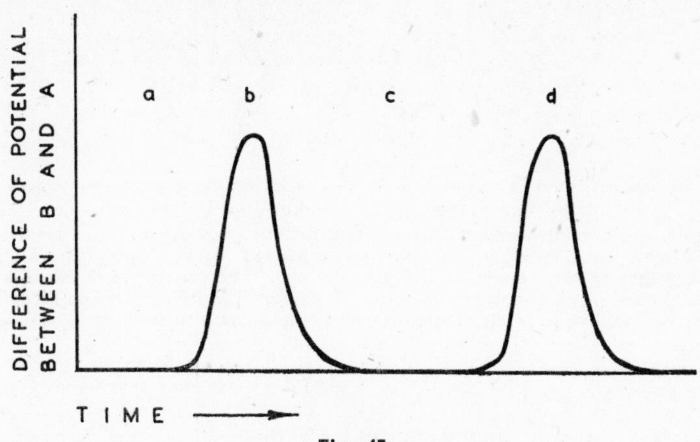

Fig. 45.
Schematic. Explanation in text.

RECORDING FROM SINGLE FIBRES OF A SIMPLE EYE

The recording of the activity of single optic fibres was first achieved with eyes having a much simpler structure than the human eye. As has already been seen, the human eye, like other vertebrate eyes, has elaborate relay stations between the light receptors, rods and cones, and the optic nerve fibres, which alone are easily amenable to experiment.

The nervous arrangements in some invertebrate eyes are much less complex. In the eye of the king crab (*Limulus Polyphemus*) illustrated in magnified section in Fig. 46, fibres run uninterruptedly from the visual cells, thus forming the optic nerve, without the interposition of any relay stations. Such an eye is a primitive faceted eye, its structure

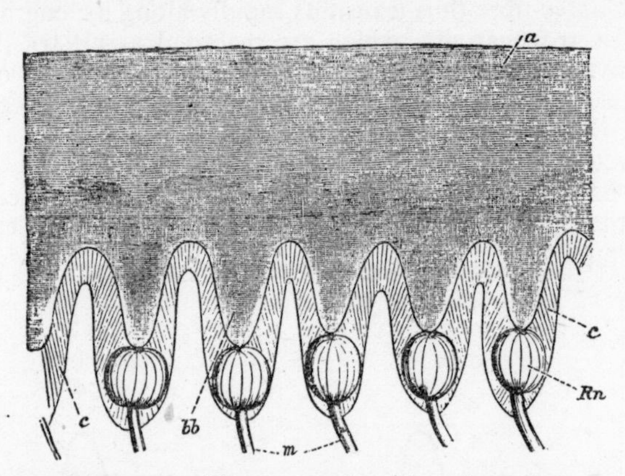

Fig. 46. Diagram of a magnified vertical section through a portion of the lateral eye of the king crab Limulus Polyphemus.

The section shows five *ommatidia* consisting each of a conical lens *bb*, a retinula *Rn* and a nerve *m*. The numerous small nerves *m*, each made up of 14 to 16 fibres, get together to form the optic nerve of the eye. The cuticle *a* and the cuticular lenses *bb* are made of a transparent horny tissue. The horizontal line at the top of the drawing, which limits the cuticle *a*, is the outside surface of the compound eye.

(After Lankester and Bourne in Lubbock (4), *On the Senses of Animals*, Kegan Paul, Trench, Trubner & Co. Ltd., London, 1899.)

and mode of functioning being similar to those of insect eyes, explained in Chapter IX. For the moment it is enough to see that the eye is made up of a number of elements, called *ommatidia*, placed side by side. Each ommatidium corresponds to one facet of the eye. Light falls directly on the ommatidia after passing through the transparent cuticle *a*. Each ommatidium contains 14 to 16 cells sensitive to light, and each cell connects directly with a nerve fibre. There are in the eye about 300 of these ommatidia, rather large and coarsely spaced, and it is relatively easy to split the nerve into its component fibres. Consequently this eye is a suitable one for experiment. The study which has been made of it will be analysed here in some detail because it is fundamental for the understanding of the electrophysiology of more complicated eyes, such as those of vertebrates.

The eye, with a margin of carapace surrounding it, is removed with an attached length of nerve of 1 to 3 centimetres. It is mounted in a

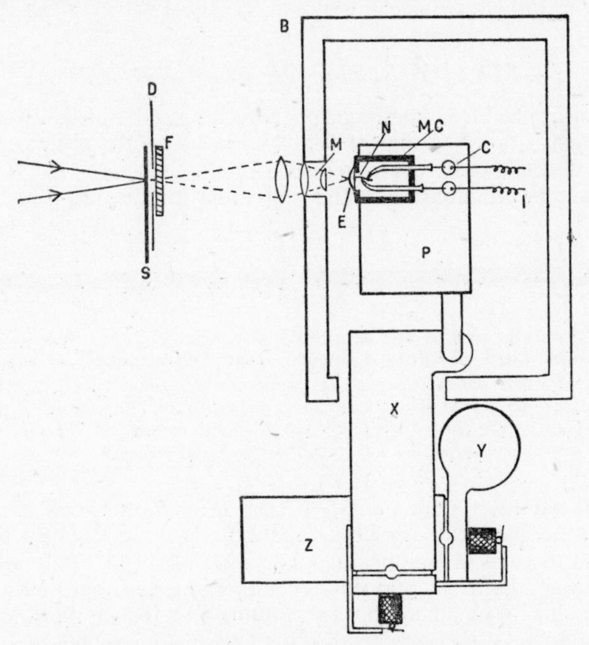

Fig. 47. Diagram of eye-nerve preparation of Limulus and apparatus.
Explanation in text.
(From Hartline and Graham (5), *J. Cell. and Comp. Physiol.*, **1**, 277, 1932.)

moist chamber MC, which is carried by a vernier micrometer manipulator XYZ, as shown in Fig. 47. The eye E can thus be moved with great accuracy, and held exactly in position relative to a source of light and a lens system M, which projects an image on to the outer surface of the eye. The nerve N is slung over two silk threads soaked in sea water, which serve as electrodes. These electrodes are connected to an amplifier, leading in turn to an oscillograph. The changes of the difference of electrical potential between two portions of the nerve are thus amplified and recorded. The nerve has previously been dissected under the microscope with glass needles. When the strand in contact with the electrodes is sufficiently thin, the oscillograph shows the typical response of one single nerve fibre, to be described presently.

STEADY STATE OF STIMULATION

Fig. 48 reproduces oscillograph recordings obtained by using an arrangement similar to that of Fig. 47. It shows the discharge of impulses in a single optic nerve fibre of Limulus, when the eye is exposed to continuous illumination. The individual impulses appear as sharp

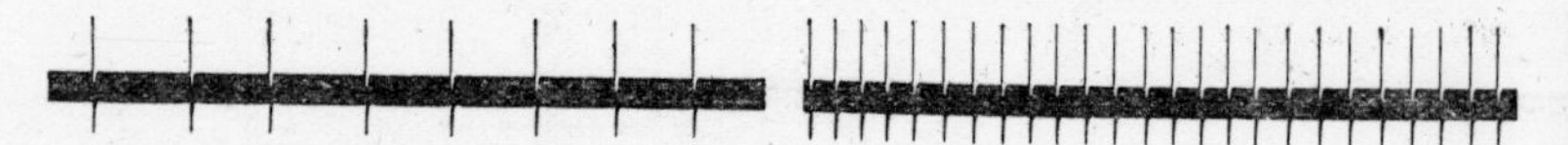

Fig. 48. Oscillograms of the amplified potential changes in a single optic nerve fibre of Limulus due to steady illumination of the eye.
Deflection upwards denotes negativity of electrode nearest the eye. Full length of each record corresponds to 1 second. Intensity of illumination is ten times greater for record on the right than for record on the left.
(From Hartline (6), *J. Opt. Soc. Amer.*, **30**, 239, 1940.)

"spikes," narrower than the peaks shown in the diagram of Fig. 45; but this difference is due solely to the different time-scale used. (Each impulse in these records appears as a double deflection, above and below the base line, due to a slight difference of technique: both electrodes A and B having been placed on an uninjured region of the fibre.) The great regularity of these recordings is their chief characteristic. All the " spikes " are identical, and the time interval separating any two spikes in each recording is constant. In these experiments the conditions under which the sensitive end cells of the Limulus eye are stimulated by light are maintained constant and the eye has been allowed time to adapt itself to the illumination. In such a " steady state " of stimulation, the nerve fibre connected to the end cell thus discharges a continuous series of electrical impulses, which are all identical and which form a regular temporal sequence. If a different light intensity is used, the only difference observed in the activity of the fibre is a change in the frequency of the discharge of impulses. For example, this frequency in the record on the left of Fig. 48 is 8 impulses per second, in the record on the right it is 25 per second, while the stimulating light is ten times more intense in the latter than in the former case. The duration of one single spike is of the order of a thousandth of a second; its height on the record corresponds to a difference of potential of about a thousandth of a volt.

PROOF THAT THE RECORDING REFERS TO A SINGLE FIBRE

It is possible to localize the particular ommatidium in the eye which corresponds to the nerve-fibre being studied. Instead of a large image illuminating the whole eye, a pinhole image of the source of light can be projected on it. The surface of the eye can then be explored point by point with this small light spot. In this way it is found that the fibre will only respond when the light spot falls on one particular ommatidium, and that the activity so elicited is the same as when the whole eye is illuminated.

When a nerve preparation giving a response such as that of Fig. 48 has been obtained, it is sometimes possible to effect a further subdivision of the nervous strand from which the recording is made. In this case, it is found that one of the new strands gives the same record as before, while the other strand is inactive.

By reducing the light intensity more and more, the number of impulses per unit of time can be decreased, until eventually no impulses are recorded. But it is not possible in this way to elicit new kinds of impulses.

All this evidence proves that in these experiments one is really dealing with a single nerve-fibre, thrown into activity when its corresponding end cell is stimulated by light.

RECORDING FROM TWO NERVE FIBRES AT THE SAME TIME

Fig. 49 shows records made with a preparation containing two nerve fibres having their end cells in two different ommatidia. When the spot of light falls on only one of these ommatidia, a recording related to a single fibre is obtained (*A*; *B*). The spikes corresponding to these two fibres have not the same height, which may be due, in part at least, to differences in the way the fibres make contact with the electrodes. When light is made to fall on both ommatidia simultaneously, the third recording, *C*, is obtained. Using the difference in height of the spikes as a criterion, it is easy to distinguish in the record the two series of impulses due to the two different fibres. When recordings are made from a whole nerve, the spikes of all the component fibres are recorded simultaneously, in the same way as those of two fibres are recorded in *C*, and give a complicated composite record.

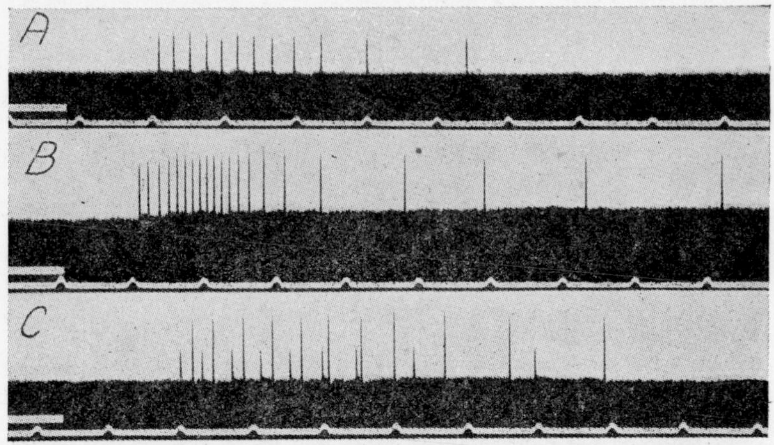

Fig. 49. Action potentials from a nerve strand of Limulus containing two active fibres.

A and *B*. Stimulation of respective end organs separately. Intensity 0.1.
C. Stimulation of both end organs simultaneously. Intensity 0.03.
Blackening of the white line on the left indicates the onset of illumination. Lower white line indicates time in fifths of second.
(After Hartline and Graham (5), *J. Cell. and Comp. Physiol.*, **1**, 277, 1932.)

SOME FURTHER CHARACTERISTICS OF THE RESPONSE IN LIMULUS

The recordings just discussed do not refer to the steady discharge of impulses, shown in Fig. 48, which becomes established after a certain time under steady conditions of stimulation by light. They show rather how the discharge begins and establishes itself after the light has just been switched on. The first impulse occurs a certain length of time after the light is switched on—later when the stimulating light is dimmer. The frequency of the impulses may then rise quickly to a maximum, and afterwards decreases, rapidly at first, and then more slowly. Eventually a constant value is reached, when the " steady

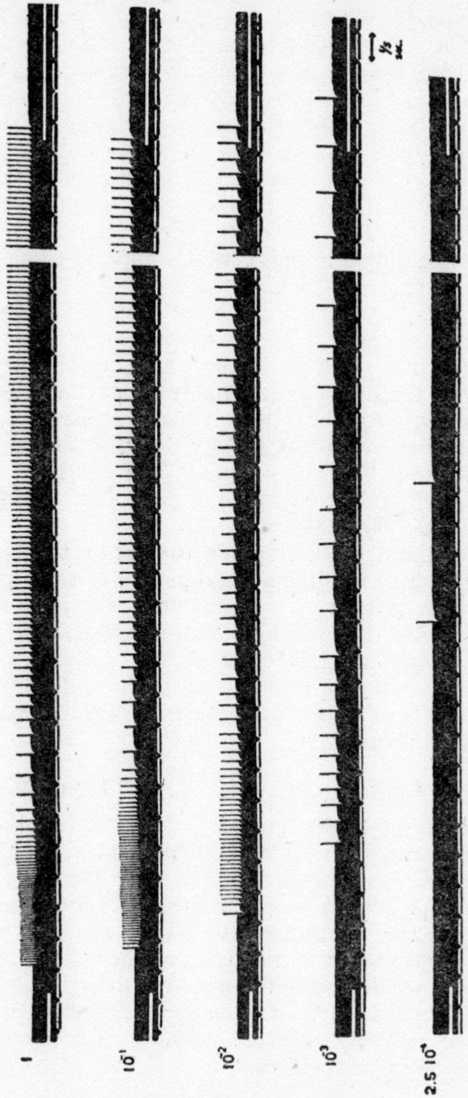

Fig. 50. Action potentials in a single fibre from the eye of Limulus, in response to illumination of its attached sense cell by lights of various intensities.

Relative intensities are given at the left of each record. The time marker beats 1/5 seconds ; above its record is the signal marking the period of illumination (the white line disappears while the light is shining). After the initial burst of impulses, there is, at high intensities, a relatively " silent " period (not mentioned in text) in which fewer impulses are discharged than before or after. The silent period is not observed in light-adapted preparations.

From Hartline (7), *Cold Spring Harbor Symposia on Quantitative Biology*, **3**, 245, 1935.)

state" of Fig. 48 is attained. When the light is cut off, the discharge of impulses persists for a very brief period, and then stops abruptly.

Fig. 50 shows these characteristics in the nervous response elicited by light of various intensities. At lower intensities the number of impulses is lower both in the initial burst and in the steady discharge. The discharge also tends to be irregular. At very low intensities, the discharge is reduced to a few impulses corresponding to the initial burst, and then stops completely in spite of the fact that the illumination of the ommatidium continues unaltered. Just above the threshold, the whole response is reduced to one single impulse, which appears some time after the light is switched on.

The impulse frequency, either in the initial burst or in the steady discharge, can be compared with the corresponding intensity of the stimulating light. It is found that, at least in the intermediate range of intensity, the frequency of the impulses is roughly proportional to the logarithm of the intensity. As the latter increases, therefore, the frequency increases also, but much less rapidly. The maximum frequency observed is 130 impulses per second. The range of light intensities for which a fibre connected to an ommatidium discharges impulses may be from 1 to 1,000,000.

All these properties of the nervous response to light on the part of the visual system of Limulus fit into the general picture of sense-organ activity. The nature of the response is fundamentally the same in all nerve fibres. Fibres connected to any sensory end-cell are always found to respond with such-like brief impulses to stimulation of their end-cell. Variation in the temporal sequence of impulses is the only form of variation of which the activity of a fibre is capable in answer to variation in intensity of the physical stimulation.

"ON" AND "OFF" FIBRES IN THE VERTEBRATE EYE

Recordings of the activity of single optic nerve-fibres of vertebrates, such as the frog, have also been obtained by the same kind of technique. Some of the fibres give responses to light of the same kind as those described for Limulus: the discharge of impulses begins soon after the light is switched on to the eye, continues with a low frequency while the light is shining, and stops soon after the light is switched off. Such is the behaviour which one would generally expect. Strikingly different behaviour has, however, been discovered in many of the fibres, which must be ascribed to the complicated nervous connexions between the photo-receptors and the optic nerve-fibres.

Most astonishing is the case of the fibres which do not respond at all when the light is switched on and while it is shining continuously, but give a brief burst of impulses just after the light has been switched *off*; these are known as " off-fibres."

" Off-fibres " respond only if the light by which they are stimulated before they give their " off " discharge was intense enough. Therefore, it cannot be said that one is dealing here with a receptive system responding to an " absence of stimulus," or some similar impossible arrangement. It is clear that the explanation of the phenomenon must be on the following lines. Some form of stimulating process is built up while the light is shining, and manifests itself when the sudden change, occurring when the light is cut off, causes a rupture of equilibrium.

" Off-fibres " also give discharges when the intensity of the light is suddenly decreased, or when a spot of light is moved across their " receptive field " in the retina, or again when a shadow moves across their receptive field, otherwise continuously illuminated. They presumably constitute a mechanism which plays an active rôle in the detection of objects in motion. Fibres of this type may function in the human eye also, " since things in motion sooner catch the eye than what not stirs " (9).

There is also in the frog a third kind of fibre, an " on-and-off fibre," which gives brief bursts of impulses both when the light is switched on and when it is switched off, and is inactive during continuous light stimulation (Fig 51).

Each fibre has a fixed type of response: and " off-fibre " does not turn into an " ordinary " fibre, and vice versa. Different types of fibres correspond to closely adjacent retinal regions. The same main

Fig. 51. " On and off " fibre in the frog retina.

The fibre responds only when the light is switched on and when it is switched off. There is no discharge during steady illumination if the stimulus spot is stationary. The signal marking the period of illumination blackens the white strip above time marker. Time in 1/5 seconds. (" Off " fibres give a similar record with regard to the second burst of impulses, but the first burst is entirely absent.)

(From Hartline (8), *Amer. J. Physiol.*, **130**, 690, 1940.)

types of response are observed in the fibres of other retinae, for instance, in the pure-cone retina of the snake.

Such peculiar responses are apparently never observed in fibres connected directly with a sensory cell as in the case of Limulus. The existence of the "off" response shows that the processes occurring in such nerve structures as the bipolar cells of the retina is complex, and that some of these structures at least do not act as simple relay stations.

RECEPTIVE FIELD OF A FIBRE IN THE VERTEBRATE EYE

In the case of Limulus, the ommatidium to which a nerve fibre is connected can be located by exploring the surface of the eye with a light

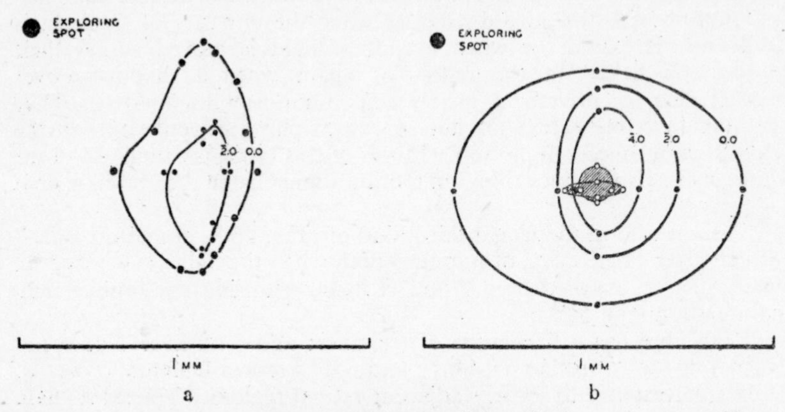

Fig. 52. Charts of the retinal regions supplying single optic nerve fibres in the eye of the frog.

a. Determination of the contours of the receptive field of a fibre at two levels of intensity of exploring spot. Dots mark positions at which exploring spot (50μ in diameter) would just elicit discharges of impulses, at the intensity whose logarithm is given on the respective curve (unit intensity = 2×10^4 metre candles). No responses at log I = − 3.0, for any location of exploring spot. This fibre responded only at "on" and "off". (Cf. Fig. 51.)

b. Contours (determined by four points on perpendicular diameters) of receptive field of a fibre, at three levels of intensity (value of log I given on respective contours). In this fibre steady stimulation (log I = 0.0 and − 2.0) produced a maintained discharge of impulses for positions of exploring spots within the central shaded area ; elsewhere discharge subsided in 1 to 2 seconds. No maintained discharge in response to intensities less than log I = − 2.0 ; no responses at all to an intensity log I = − 4.6.

(From Hartline (8), *Amer. J. Physiol.*, **130**, 690, 1940.)

spot. Similarly, it is possible to find the region of the retina of a frog which must receive light in order to stimulate a given nerve-fibre. This region is called the " receptive field " of the fibre. The receptive field of the optic nerve-fibres have a definite localization in the retina, but they have a very appreciable extent, being of the order of 1 mm. across. As shown in Fig. 52, all parts of a receptive field are not equally sensitive. A much stronger light intensity must be applied at its periphery than at its centre in order to obtain a threshold stimulation. There is summation of the effects of light falling in different parts of the receptive field. The receptive fields of different nerve-fibres overlap to some extent on the retina: a spot of light falling on the retina may stimulate several fibres simultaneously. The very many rods and cones contained in the total retinal area corresponding to the receptive field of a fibre, therefore, are probably not all connected to this particular fibre. Even so, by referring to the data of Chapter II, it appears that the receptors connected to one single optic nerve-fibre must number thousands, or tens of thousands, of rods. All types of fibres in the frog's eye have receptive fields of this kind.

BIBLIOGRAPHY

(1) ADRIAN, E. D. (1928). *The Basis of Sensation*, London.

(2) ADRIAN, E. D. (1932). *The Mechanism of Nervous Action*, London and Philadelphia.

(3) HARTLINE, H. K. (1942). " The neural mechanisms for vision," *The Harvey Lectures*, **37**, 39–68.

(4) LUBBOCK, SIR J. (Lord Avebury) (1899). *On the Senses, Instincts and Intelligence of Animals, with special reference to Insects*, London.

(5) HARTLINE, H. K., and GRAHAM, C. H. (1932). "Nerve impulses from single receptors in the eye," *J. Cell. and Comp. Physiol.*, **1**, 277–295.

(6) HARTLINE, H. K. (1940). " The nerve messages in the fibers of the visual pathway," *J. Opt. Soc. Amer.*, **30,** 239–247.

(7) HARTLINE, H. K. (1935). " The discharge of nerve impulses from the single visual sense cell," *Cold Spring Harbor Symposia on Quantitative Biology*, **3,** 245–250.

(8) HARTLINE, H. K. (1940). " The receptive fields of optic nerve fibers," *Amer. J. Physiol.*, **130,** 690–699.

(9) SHAKESPEARE, *Troilus and Cressida*, III, iii, 183.

Chapter VI

THE MINIMUM ENERGY NECESSARY FOR VISION

SENSITIVITY OF THE EYE IN ASTRONOMY

EARLY astronomers had to depend exclusively on visual observations, and accordingly, astronomical circles have always been interested in the properties of the eye. When we look at the night sky, the dimmest stars that we can see are stars of the sixth magnitude. Dimmer stars can be seen with the naked eye if special precautions are taken. Astronomers have found that if an observer is placed in a dark room having only a very small opening towards the night sky, he can see stars of magnitude 7, 8 and even 8·5 (1). This is so because the stars are then seen against a dark background: it is the brightness of the sky on which the stars appear which prevents us from seeing these dim stars under ordinary conditions of observation.

The magnitude of a star defines, on a special logarithmic scale, the illumination produced by the star on the earth. The stellar magnitude of the sun has been determined on the same scale (2). From these data one can derive at once that the illumination produced by the faintest star we can see with the naked eye is about 10^{-14} times that produced by the sun (3). This means that the earth receives from the faintest star, per unit area, an amount of light which is one hundred million million times less than that received from the sun. The range of illumination within which the human eye can function thus extends over about 14 logarithmic units, since it is possible to look directly at the sun for an instant.

The eye is therefore very sensitive to light. For it will be remembered that the sun sends us a total energy flux (visible and invisible radiating energy) of about two gram-calories per minute and per square centimetre; and two calories are sufficient to raise the temperature of one cubic centimetre of water by only two degrees centigrade.

Experiments on the sensitivity of the eye can of course be carried out entirely in the laboratory. By using " artificial stars ", that is, dim point sources of light, it is found that a man can see a source of light which is as faint as a standard candle seen from a distance of 27 kilometres through a non-absorbing atmosphere (4). Incidentally, using this value, it is easy to arrive at the result that a powerful searchlight directed from the moon to the earth should be visible here with the naked eye (2).

The standard candle is the unit of luminous intensity. It used to be defined by a flame burning under controlled conditions. To-day it is defined by means of incandescent electric lamps kept in various national standardising laboratories (5). Now, even though we thus know the sensitivity of the eye in relation to a reproducible terrestrial source of light, this does not give directly the eye sensitivity in terms of energy units, even if the energy emitted by the lamp has been measured. For a standard lamp emits radiations of many different wave-lengths, to which, as we have seen, the eye is very unequally sensitive. The matter is further complicated by the fact that the rod sensitivity curve, valid at low intensities, is different from the cone sensitivity curve valid at the intensities generally used in photometric calibrations.

Nevertheless, knowing the limit of visibility of a standard candle, it is possible to determine the order of magnitude of the minimum flux of energy which must strike the eye for a point source of light to be seen. It is 10^{-9} erg per second (6). It will be remembered that 1 erg is approximately equal to the energy necessary for lifting a mass of 1 milligram to a height of one centimetre. Thus, an amount of light energy one thousand million times smaller than this, falling into the eye every second, is still able to stimulate the retina.

COMPARISON OF THE EYE WITH ARTIFICIAL DETECTORS OF LIGHT

Direct measurements of radiating energy, such as visible light, are often made by using a thermopile. A part of this instrument is placed in the beam of light to be measured. Its blackened surface absorbs the luminous energy falling upon it and transforms it into heat. This heat in turn raises the temperature of the corresponding part of the thermopile. It is then the property of the instrument that this difference of temperature produces an electric current. The greater the rise in temperature, the more intense is this current, which can be measured by a galvanometer. The greater the light intensity, therefore, the greater, finally, will be the galvanometer deflection. Unlike the eye, the thermopile reacts indiscriminately to radiations of all wave-lengths in proportion to their intensity, but it is much less sensitive. The most sensitive thermopile needs a flux of energy of about 10^{-2} erg per second to give a galvanometer deflection. The eye is thus ten million times more sensitive than the thermopile (2). This is one of the reasons why it is often found convenient to use the eye itself in photometric measurements—while one would never for a moment think of using muscular sensitivity in precision measurements of weight.

The photoelectric cells, the principle of which is explained in the next chapter, are selective detectors of light. Unlike the thermopile, but like the eye, such cells are unequally sensitive to radiations of different wave-lengths. They have a greater sensitivity than thermopiles, but it is doubtful if any of them, or, in fact, if any artificial detector of light, reaches a sensitivity as high as that of the eye.

The photographic plate is another selective and sensitive detector of light. Its sensitivity, however, is mainly due to its cumulative properties. When two light exposures are made in succession on a plate, the effect of the second adds itself to that of the first. Very long exposure times thus allow the detection of very weak but continuous sources of light (7).

It may be remarked that it is fortunate for us that our retina does not possess such cumulative properties. If it did, we would see, not what is before us here and now, but a composite of all the scenes that have confronted us ever since we were born, all superimposed one on another, in the same way as it is possible to superimpose several pictures on the photographic plate of a camera.

TEMPORAL SUMMATION IN THE RETINA

As a matter of fact, *temporal summation* in the eye does not extend over exposures longer than about $1/10$ of a second (while for the photographic plate it extends over indefinitely long exposures). If, for instance, the threshold of a small area of the periphery of the retina is measured using the method described in Chapter III, it is found that, when the duration of the flash is more than about $1/2$ second, the light *intensity* must reach a certain value, independent of the length of the exposure, in order that the test field be seen. When longer exposure times are used, correspondingly greater *quantities* of light become therefore necessary. If the exposure time is doubled while the intensity is halved, the field is not seen. There is no summation over such lengths of time.

The position is quite different for exposures shorter than about $^1/_{20}$ second. In this case all that matters is the product of the exposure time by the light intensity, that is, the *total quantity of light* striking the retina. During such brief exposures, temporal summation is complete, or in other words, the effects of light on the retina are quite cumulative. For instance, the threshold is reached and the field is seen both when the duration is 0·03 second and the intensity 1, in arbitrary units, and when the duration is 0·0003 second and the intensity is 100 units. In the intermediate region between $^1/_{20}$ and $^1/_2$ second, incomplete summation occurs (8).

It will be noted that the smallest quantities of light are needed to reach the threshold when the exposure times are shorter than $^1/_{20}$ second. The time during which summation of the effects of light occurs, about $^1/_{10}$ second, is called *retinal action time* (9).

EFFECT OF EYE MOVEMENTS

The existence of the saccadic movements of the eye must be borne in mind in connexion with experiments on the visibility of such light sources as stars. The eye moves very rapidly, and stops at a given position for a duration of the order of $^1/_{10}$ second, which is similar to the retinal action time. Then the eye moves rapidly again, followed by another brief stop; then on again, and so on.

When we look at a star in the ordinary way, therefore, a successive series of discrete pictures of the star is formed on various points of the retina, each picture being made with an exposure time of the order of $^1/_{10}$ second. This is enough to show that the measurements mentioned above, however interesting from a practical point of view, are not well controlled from a physiological point of view. In particular, if we look at a star for a minute or so, only a few of the hundreds of discrete light pictures of the star formed on the retina during this time may have reached the threshold. By prolonging the time of observation the chance of having at least one threshold exposure increases. Accordingly, dimmer stars may be seen when the time of observation is increased, this effect occurring purely on grounds of probability, without any temporal summation of the effects of light over such protracted periods —periods, which in fact, are much longer than the retinal action time.

These considerations show how complex may be the phenomena taking place in the eye in apparently simple situations. They also show that, in order to determine the minimum energy necessary for the stimulation of the retina, the method of flash and fixation described in Chapter III must be used. And it is also clear, that to reach genuine minimum energy values, the duration of the flash in these experiments must be shorter than the retinal action time.

MEASUREMENT OF THE MINIMUM ENERGY NECESSARY FOR VISION

It is a complicated task to measure the exact value of the least amount of light energy capable of eliciting a visual response when it falls into the human eye. As we have just seen, it cannot be done simply by measuring the energy of a continuous light source which is just visible. Such an apparently simple arrangement is greatly lacking in precision from a physiological point of view. In fact, it is found necessary to use complicated apparatus and to take elaborate precautions in order to ensure that the physiological situation will be simple and well-defined. The experimental conditions leading to the lowest possible threshold value must then be carefully chosen.

About a dozen investigations have been made on this problem. The first was made in 1889 by Langley, the American astrophysicist. He had invented the bolometer (10), an instrument which made it possible, for the first time, to measure radiating energy. The bolometer is still used to-day, much in the same way as the thermopile. In a remarkable piece of investigation, Langley very soon used his new instrument to measure the sensitivity of the eye (11). Among the various subsequent determinations of the absolute threshold of the human eye, those which were made in the most critical manner, give results which are in good agreement with one another. It is worth describing in some detail a recent investigation of this kind (12).

Apparatus: Fig. 53 shows the apparatus which was used. The light source L is a ribbon filament lamp run on constant current. By means of a lens the light is focussed on the slit of a double monochromator M_1M_2, and finally falls on the artificial pupil P. The double monochromator is a double spectroscope. The white light which the lamp emits has an extended continuous spectrum, while that which emerges from the monochromator is monochromatic, and its wave-length can be chosen at will by the observer. (See Chapter XII, on Newton's doctrine of colour.)

The subject of the experiment sits in a dark cabinet in the dark room. His head is held in a fixed position in the following way.

An impression of his upper jaw is taken in hard wax before the experiment, and rigidly attached to the apparatus. When he sits for the experiment, the subject takes this dental impression between his teeth. His left eye is next to the artificial pupil *P*. When he looks through the artificial pupil at the red fixation point *FP*, he sees laterally the

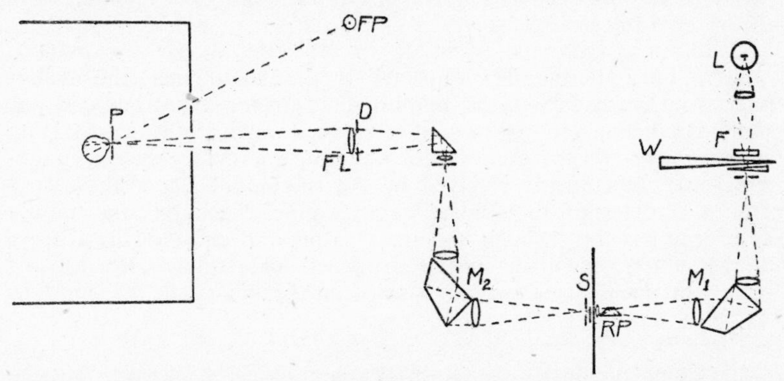

Fig. 53. Optical system for measuring minimum energies necessary for vision.

The eye at the pupil *P* fixates the red point *FP* and observes the test field formed by the lens *FL* and the diaphragm *D*. The light for this field comes from the lamp *L* through the neutral filter *F* and wedge *W*, through the double monochromator M_1M_2, and is controlled by the shutter *S*. See text.

(From Hecht, Shlaer and Pirenne (12), *J. Gen. Physiol.*, **25**, 819, 1942.)

field lens *FL*. The artificial pupil is simply a circular hole, 2 mm. in diameter, drilled in a metal plate. As this is smaller than the pupil of the eye, the variations in the size of the latter need not be taken into account in the measurements.

In this way the position of the head is fixed by the use of the dental impression. The position of the eye in its orbit is fixed, and is the same each time the subject directs his gaze on the fixation point, as has been explained in Chapter III. The image of the test field limited by the diaphragm *D* is thus always made to fall on exactly the same point of the retina.

Using such an arrangement, the lens *FL* is seen by the subject as a uniformly illuminated surface. The light intensity of this field is varied in large steps by changing the neutral filters *F*, and in a gradual way by changing the position of the neutral wedge *W*. The neutral filters and wedge are made of dark glass which absorbs part of the light of the lamp *L*. The exact amount of light which they allow to pass for any setting has been previously measured. The exposure time is fixed by the precision shutter *S*, which allows the light to pass through the monochromator for one thousandth of a second, when the subject releases the key.

Calibrations are made essentially by replacing the eye and artificial pupil *P* by a thermopile, connected to a galvanometer, the neutral filters and wedges and the diaphragm *D* being removed, and the shutter *S* being kept open. By comparison with a standard lamp emitting a known total amount of radiating energy, the flux of monochromatic light energy received by the thermopile under these conditions is determined. Simple computations then give the amount of energy passing through the artificial pupil *P* and striking the eye of the subject, when the shutter is opened for a single flash, for any setting of the wedges, and any size of diaphragm *D*.

Physiological Conditions of the Experiment: These were—

(1) Complete dark adaptation of the eye. The subject waits in total darkness for three-quarters of an hour before the experiments are begun. This is obviously necessary, for the sensitivity of the eye is much lower after it has been exposed to light, and increases rapidly at first, more slowly later, when the subject is left in the dark (13, 14). This phenomenon is very noticeable when one comes from daylight into a cinema. After half an hour in the dark, if the light to which the eye has been previously exposed was not very intense, the eye sensitivity, which may by then have increased by a factor of 10,000, varies very little.

(2) The use of monochromatic radiation of 510 mμ. This wavelength corresponds to the maximum of the sensitivity curve of the rods. Using any other wave-length, larger amounts of energy would be necessary to reach the threshold of the dark-adapted eye (cf. Fig. 40).

(3) A peripheral region of the retina containing a very high density of rods. A region 20° laterally is chosen (see Chapter II). Such a region is found to be very sensitive to light, as has been seen in Chapter III.

(4) A test field—defined by the diaphragm *D*—having a diameter subtending an angle of 10 minutes of arc at the eye, is used. This is

placed, in accordance with (3) above, 20° peripherally to the fixation point. Using a field 10 minutes in diameter, it is found that the total amount of light necessary to reach the threshold is minimal. The product of the area by the light intensity must be higher when large, instead of small, fields are used. The situation resembles that of temporal summation, in that the total amount of energy tends to become roughly constant when small fields are used, as when brief exposures are used. In the present case this is only an approximation, however, and it appears that the use of a 10′ field leads to the smallest threshold values (12).

(5) A flash duration of $^1/_{1000}$ second. The reasons for using such a brief exposure are given in the preceding sections.

Psychological Conditions: From the subject's point of view, the experiment takes place as follows. The subject first waits for three-quarters of an hour in the dark room. He is then told by the observer (who controls the current in the lamp, etc.) that conditions are set and that he should try a flash when ready. The subject then takes the dental impression between his teeth, and looks at the red fixation point through the artificial pupil. Nothing but this fixation point is visible in the surrounding darkness. At the moment which he considers propitious, when his gaze is fixed exactly on the red point, the subject releases the lever which operates the shutter. This flashes the light on the small lateral field, and if the light is intense enough, the subject sees it " out of the corner of his eye " (cf. Fig. 35). The subject reports whether or not he has seen the flash, and the result is recorded. The experiment is then repeated at another light intensity obtained by changing the setting of the wedge. (Preliminary trials are of course made before starting the actual measurement.) Fixation of the red point need not be continuous, a circumstance which avoids undue fatigue. This is important because a great number of trials must be made at one sitting to obtain the curve giving the frequency with which the flash is seen at various intensities; as will be seen in Chapter VIII, this curve is a very important feature of the experiment. For the present, suffice it to say that it is not possible to find an intensity at which the flash is always seen, while it is never seen for a slightly lower intensity. The minimum energy was therefore taken as the energy content of the flashes which are seen in a proportion of the trials equal to 60 per cent. in any given sitting.

Results: The results obtained in this way vary from subject to subject. Moreover, in one and the same subject, they are found to vary from time to time as the measurements are repeated. In a series of measurements extending over one year and a half, for instance, one subject was found to require at different times flash energy contents of

$$4{\cdot}83;\ 5{\cdot}18;\ 4{\cdot}11;\ 3{\cdot}34;\ 3{\cdot}03;\ 4{\cdot}72;\ \text{and}\ 5{\cdot}68 \times 10^{-10}\ \text{erg},$$

in order to see the flash with a frequency of 60 per cent. Notice that the extremes of this series are in a ratio of almost 2 to 1. Such day-to-day variations of the visual threshold in one individual are often observed, and when the conditions are sufficiently controlled, as in this case, they cannot be attributed to experimental errors. They are caused by biological changes in the organism, and are not to be confused with the variability of response of any one individual in one single sitting, mentioned above and discussed in Chapter VIII.

For seven subjects, the measurements thus obtained of the minimum necessary energy for vision led to values ranging between

$$2{\cdot}1\ \text{and}\ 5{\cdot}7 \times 10^{-10}\ \text{erg (12).}$$

These values are close to the values found in other critical investigations. This corresponds also to the order of magnitude, 10^{-9} erg. per second, derived from the visibility of star-like sources.

The smallness of the minimum energy necessary for vision becomes clear if one remembers that an erg is quite a small amount of energy —being approximately equal to the work necessary to lift 1 milligram to a height of 1 centimetre. The mechanical energy of a pea falling from a height of one inch, would, if transformed into luminous energy, be sufficient to give a faint impression of light to every man that ever lived.

The real significance of these energies will be apparent when the action of the light upon the retina is examined, in connexion with the quantum theory of radiation.

BIBLIOGRAPHY AND NOTES

(1) CURTIS, H. D. (1901). " On the limits of unaided vision," *Lick Observatory Bulletin*, **2,** 67–69.

(2) FABRY, C. (1934). " Les principes de la photométrie en astronomie et en physique," *Mémorial des Sciences Physiques*, xxiv.

(3) The magnitude m of a star is defined by the equation

$$\log I = A - 0{\cdot}4m$$

where I is the illumination produced at the eye by the star, and A is a numerical constant.

The stellar magnitude of the sun is – 26·7.

The ratio of illuminations produced by the sun and by a star of magnitude 8·5 has therefore a logarithm equal to

$$0{\cdot}4 \times (26{\cdot}7 + 8{\cdot}5) = 14.$$

(4) BUISSON, H. (1917). "The minimum radiation visually perceptible," *Astrophys, J.*, **46**, 296.

(5) WALSH, J. W. T. (1926). *Photometry*, 505 pp., London.

(6) RUSSELL, H. N. (1917). "The minimum radiation visually perceptible," *Astrophys. J.*, **45**, 60–64.

(7) In X-ray investigations, an exposure time of more than 2,000 hours has been used in order to obtain a photograph of a very faint X-ray spectrum. (DU MOND, J. W. M., and KIRKPATRICK, H. A. (1937), *Phys. Rev.*, **52**, 419–436.)

(8) GRAHAM, C. H., and MARGARIA, R. (1935). "Area and the intensity-time relation in the peripheral retina," *Amer. J. Physiol.*, **113**, 302–305.

(9) The retinal action time must not be confused with the period of time during which the light of a brief flash appears subjectively to remain present after the flash is over. "After images" which occur after one has looked at a bright light, for instance, the setting sun, also are quite a different phenomenon.

(10) LANGLEY, S. P. (1881). "The bolometer and radiant energy," *Proc. Am. Acad. Sc.*, **16**, 342.

(11) LANGLEY, S. P. (1889). "Energy and vision," *Phil. Mag.*, **27**, series 5, 1.

(12) HECHT, S., SHLAER, S., and PIRENNE, M. H. (1942). "Energy, Quanta, and Vision," *J. General Physiol.*, **25**, 819–840.

(13) HECHT, S. (1937). "Rods, Cones and the Chemical Basis of Vision," *Physiol. Rev.*, **17**, 239.

(14) MANDELBAUM, J. (1941). "Dark Adaptation, some physiologic and clinical considerations," *Archives of Ophthalmology, Chicago*, **26**, 203–239.

Chapter VII

LIGHT QUANTA AND THE RETINA

QUANTUM THEORY

THE experiments related in the preceding chapter show that the minimum amount of light energy necessary for vision is remarkably small. The question may then be asked: Is it possible that this threshold energy could be much lower still, or is there a natural limit to the smallest amount of light which can act upon an organism?

In electrical experiments, it is impossible to deal with amounts of electricity smaller than the charge of an electron. In chemical experiments it is impossible to deal with an amount less than one molecule of a given substance. According to classical physics, the situation would have appeared to be different in the case of light. Luminous energy being regarded as of the nature of a continuum, there would be no limit to the smallness of the quantity of light capable of interaction with matter. The conception of modern physics, however, is radically different. Radiation is considered to behave in its interaction with matter as if it had, like matter itself, a corpuscular structure. Accordingly there is an absolute natural limit to the amount of light which can be used in experiments, as there is to the amount of electricity or chemical substance. This smallest possible amount of light is *one quantum*. It is from the point of view of this discontinuous structure of light that the threshold values of the eye acquire their full significance.

A brief discussion of the photoelectric effect may prove helpful in trying to understand the quantum nature of light. If a metal such as sodium or potassium is illuminated by light of short wave-length, it emits electrons from its surface. These can be easily detected in the following way. The metal is used as an electrode in a glass cell, which contains another electrode, both electrodes being in a high vacuum, with a suitable potential applied to them. A current passes through the vacuum every time the metal emits electrons. Now, it is observed that the current passes—thus proving the emission of electrons—only when the wave-length of the light falling on the metal is below a certain critical value. If the wave-length is too long, no electrons are emitted, no matter how high the intensity of the light may be. The deciding factor is not therefore the *amount* of light, but the wave-length. Now, according to quantum theory, the quanta of light of short wave-length are larger than those of light of long wave-length. The explanation of the photoelectric effect is then, the action of individual quanta on individual electrons of the metal. As a certain definite amount of energy is necessary to expel an electron, the light quantum interacting with the metal in the cell must have sufficient energy. This in turn means that the wave-length of the light must be sufficiently short. If the wave-length is longer than the critical value, none of the quanta will have the requisite energy to expel an electron. Each quantum acts independently on the metal.

The energy of a quantum of a radiation of frequency ν is proportional to the frequency ν, being equal to $h\nu$, where h is an universal constant, known as Planck's *constant of action*, equal to $6{\cdot}62 \times 10^{-27}$ erg $\times$ second. The frequency ν is equal to the velocity of light, c, divided by the wave-length λ. The magnitude of the quantum of a radiation is thus inversely proportional to the wave-length of the radiation: for instance, the energy of a quantum of violet light of wave-length $400m\mu$ is twice as large as that of a quantum of red light of wave-length $800m\mu$.

NUMBER OF QUANTA ABSORBED BY THE RODS

For a wave-length of 510 $m\mu$, the quantum $h\nu$ is $3{\cdot}89 \times 10^{-12}$ erg. Comparing this to the threshold energy values found in the preceding Chapter, where light of this wave-length was used, it is immediately found that these energies correspond to a number of quanta ranging from 54 to 148, striking the cornea of the eye. This is not a large number, but it is still considerably higher than the number of quanta which finally act upon the nervous system, that is, which are absorbed by the rods of the retina (1).

When the light strikes the cornea there is a loss of about 5 per cent. at the interface between the air and the cornea: this proportion of the light is reflected outwards and does not enter the eye. More important are the losses suffered by absorption as the light goes through the optical media of the eye: cornea, aqueous humour, lens, vitreous humour. These media are not as transparent as one might suppose, and in fact absorb about 50 per cent. of the light used in the experiment discussed here. Taking account of these losses, it is found that the number of quanta reaching the retina in the experiments ranges from 26 to 70.

Now, even this number of quanta actually reaching the retina is not all involved in the process of excitation of the retina, because the visual purple present in the rods does not absorb more than 10 or 20 per cent. of the light. As much as 80 or 90 per cent. of it may pass through the layer of rods (which is only about 0·05 mm. thick) without being absorbed by the visual purple and without therefore producing any effect on this substance or on the rods. The proportion of light thus lost is absorbed by the black pigment. Its above value has been estimated in two ways, giving similar results. A direct estimate can be made on the basis of data supplied by investigators who extracted visual purple from the eyes of rats, rabbits, and even in one case, of man, and then proceeded to measure the absorption of light by the solution so obtained. An indirect estimate was obtained by comparing the shape of the visibility curve of the dark adapted eye with the shape of the spectral absorption curve of visual purple at different concentrations, as can be understood by referring to Chapter IV. These estimates involve some uncertainty in the calculations, and moreover, it is unlikely that all eyes are exactly alike in this respect. Taking the 20 per cent. absorption as an upper value, it is found that at the threshold of vision the number of quanta actually absorbed by the visual purple in the rods is only

5 to 14 quanta.

This comes decidedly nearer to the absolute limit of one quantum.

HOW THESE QUANTA ACT UPON THE RETINA

The image of a test field whose diameter subtends an angle of 10 minutes at the eye, covers on the retina an area containing about 500 rods. According to the quantum theory—as well as the wave theory—the light falls on the retina within this area; its absorption then proceeds, in the quantum theory, in a number of independent events, each single event involving one individual quantum (2). Each of the 5 to 14 quanta thus absorbed in the given retinal area has about the same chance of being absorbed in any one rod. It may therefore happen that several quanta are absorbed in the same rod. It might therefore be suggested as a possibility that a stimulation sufficiently strong for the light to be seen is produced in the optic nerve only when at least two quanta are absorbed in one and the same rod. According to this line of thought, then, the light could not be seen if all the quanta involved fell on different rods. But this suggestion must be rejected, for the following reason: in terms of the total number of rods available (500), and of the number of quanta involved, it is an easy matter to calculate the probability of having two quanta absorbed together in any one of the rods. The probability will be very small: much less than 60 per cent. in fact, which is the frequency with which the light is seen in the experiment. It follows from this that such a " double hit " cannot be a necessary condition of an adequate stimulation. Furthermore, by reducing the size of the test field, the number of rods involved is decreased. This in turn increases rapidly the probability of a double hit. Yet the threshold energy for smaller fields is about the same as that for the 10′ field. This appears to rule out the possibility that a double hit be the condition for stimulation.

Thus, the light is seen when each of the 5 to 14 quanta is absorbed in a different one of the 500 rods covered by the image of the test field.

We are thus led to enquire about the effect produced in a single rod by the absorption of one quantum. When light acts upon a chemical substance (e.g. when it bleaches visual purple) the initial process consists in the absorption of light in individual quanta by the molecules of the substance. Each quantum is absorbed by one single molecule, and causes some changes in the molecule: it may, for instance, split it in two. And the molecule thus acted on, may react on other molecules. This is a general law of photochemistry. One may therefore state that when one quantum is absorbed in one retinal rod, only one molecule of visual purple is affected in the initial stage. But this single molecule, transformed by light, may be able to start a series of physico-chemical reactions involving other molecules, and leading eventually to some form of nervous stimulation (3). *As a reactive system, a retinal rod thus reaches the absolute limit of sensitivity set by the quantum and molecular theories.*

As we have seen, anatomical studies show that in the vertebrate retina, many rods converge through the relay system on to one single fibre of the optic nerve. Electro-physiological experiments show that one nerve fibre has in the retina an extended receptive field, inside which summation of the effects of light can occur. It may be concluded, therefore, that when a number of rod cells have been stimulated, each by the absorption of a single quantum, a summation of their individual stimulations takes place at the level of the nervous relay station. The stimulation can then spread to other parts of the nervous system, and the organism responds to the flash of light.

The events which take place in the threshold experiments may therefore be tentatively imagined as follows: in each of a number of rods among the group of 500, one quantum is absorbed by one molecule of visual purple. In each of these rods, this molecule starts reactions leading to the stimulation of the nervous structure of the rod cell. A single stimulation of this kind is not capable by itself of overcoming the barrier on the way to the higher nerve centres. However, a summation of the individual stimulations occurs at the level of the bipolar cell to which the rods are connected. When the number of rods simultaneously stimulated is large enough (5 to 14) the stimulation of the bipolar cell is propagated by an optic nerve fibre to higher nerve centres, so that eventually the subject signals that he has seen the light.

It follows from what has been said in Chapter V that the lowest possible state of activity which can be produced in the optic nerve is the discharge of one single impulse by one single fibre. It is not known whether the threshold stimulation discussed here corresponds to this very minimum, or to a greater state of nervous activity. But, for any given biological state of the organism, this threshold stimulation, whatever it is, must have a certain definite value.

BIBLIOGRAPHY AND NOTES

(1) Details concerning matters discussed in this chapter will be found in: HECHT, S., SHLAER, S., and PIRENNE, M. H. (1942). "Energy, Quanta, and Vision," *J. General Physiology*, **25**, 819-840. STILES, W. S. (1944), "Current problems of visual research," *Proc. Physical Soc. London*, **56**, 329-356.

(2) It is unnecessary to say that the absorption of fractions of one quantum in different rods is impossible from the very nature of the quantum.

(3) The exact events which take place between the absorption of light and the stimulation of the nervous ending of the rod are not known.

Chapter VIII

QUANTUM FLUCTUATIONS

CONCEPT OF THE THRESHOLD

In the preceding chapter it was said that when a certain number of rods have each absorbed one quantum, the nervous stimulation becomes adequate and the light is seen; the threshold of vision is then reached. The concept of the threshold is a general and indispensable one in sensory physiology; it means that for any sense-organ there is, under given conditions, a critical intensity of stimulus which will just produce a stimulation. A stimulus as large as or larger than this threshold stimulus will produce a stimulation; a smaller stimulus will fail to do so. In the case of the stimulation of a given region of the retina by light, the retinal threshold is a certain amount of light absorbed by the retina. This, as we have seen, must be an integer number of quanta. According to the preceding chapter, its value lies between 5 and 14.

Let us assume now that this retinal threshold n is constant, and is, for instance, $n = 6$, for a given subject in a given experiment. Let us then present to this subject flashes of light of increasing intensities, graduated by using the wedge of the apparatus. It might then be expected that when the intensity of the light entering the eye is below a certain value, the subject would never see the light because his retina would absorb less than 6 quanta. For settings of the wedge giving an intensity equal to or greater than this value, on the other hand, the light would always be seen by the subject because his retina would then absorb 6 quanta or more. There would thus be a definite critical setting of the wedge at which the light would be seen, while the light would not be seen for lower settings.

But such expectations are not borne out in fact. Even in the best-controlled experiments, *there is never such a sudden jump from an intensity at which the light is never seen to an intensity at which it is always seen.* There is a smooth transition from one to the other as the setting of the wedge is progressively changed to make the light more and more intense. This region of transition has a considerable extent, far beyond any instrumental error. The intensity must be increased by a factor of about 10 to pass from conditions where the light is practically never seen to conditions where the light is almost always seen.

For any given setting of the wedge in the region of transition, it is always found that a given subject sometimes sees the light and sometimes fails to see it, however carefully the experiment is controlled. *If* now it were established that under constant physical conditions the retina always absorbed a constant amount of light—that is, a constant number of quanta—variations in the sensitivity of the subject would be the only possible explanation of such an experimental fact. It would be necessary to assume that in order that the light be seen, the retina in different trials needs to absorb different numbers of quanta. Suppose, for instance, that the apparatus were set in such a way that it would always really deliver 6 quanta to the retina. In an experiment in which the subject sees the light in only 60 per cent. of the trials the inescapable conclusion would be that the absorption of 6 quanta is sufficient in 60 per cent of the trials only, and that the subject is less sensitive, needing more than 6 quanta, in the remaining 40 per cent. of the trials. The retinal threshold n, instead of remaining constantly equal to 6, would thus be subjected to wide variations.

It will be shown, however, that *it is impossible to deliver exactly to the retina, say,* 6 *quanta, in each trial.* This invalidates the conclusion that the observed uncertainty of seeing is necessarily due to variations of the threshold.

To make the meaning of this clear, a simple analogy might perhaps be used—although it should not be pressed too far. There are slot machines which deliver a ticket when, say, 6 pennies have been inserted in the slot. As a rule, when a " stimulus " of 6 pennies is applied to a machine of this kind, it will always give, as a " response ", a sixpenny ticket. Imagine now a machine such that sometimes we do not get our ticket after inserting 6 pennies, but we get it only after inserting more than 6, say, 9 pennies. On the other hand, imagine that this machine sometimes delivers a ticket after we have inserted less than 6 pennies, say, 3 pennies, or 1 penny. The obvious conclusion would be that the state of the machine varies from time to time. Sometimes unused pennies may have been left in it; this would explain that its " threshold ", that is, the number of pennies necessary to obtain a response, is then lower than 6. At other times, the mechanism of the machine may suffer from abnormal frictions: the machine is then less sensitive and needs a greater stimulus to give a response; its threshold is higher than the normal threshold of 6 pennies.

If we insert 6 pennies in the slot and sometimes get our ticket, while at other times we do not get it, we have no doubt that the cause of this variability must be in the machine, because we know that we have placed into the slot exactly 6 pennies each time. In what concerns the stimulation of the retina by light, however, we shall see that the whole point is that it is physically impossible to deliver to it exactly the same amount of light, say, 6 quanta, in each trial. And in this case we are therefore not justified in concluding that the variability of the response—that is, the fact that at the limit of visibility a light is sometimes seen, and sometimes not seen—is necessarily due to a variability of the organism.

WHY THE NUMBER OF QUANTA ABSORBED CANNOT BE CONSTANT

On the basis of quantum theory it can be shown that it is not possible to set up conditions such that for each flash the retina would absorb a constant number of quanta, say, 6. And it would be quite as impossible to arrange for a constant number of quanta to be absorbed by any purely physical apparatus, instead of the retina. Let us assume that in a series of flashes a number of 30 quanta each time reaches the layer of rods in the retina, and that the visual purple in this layer absorbs 20 per cent. of the light incident upon it. Absorption of light—as in the photo-electric effect—occurs by independent quantum processes. An absorption of 20 per cent. means that each quantum has 20 chances in 100 of being caught by one of the molecules of visual purple, and 80 chances of passing through the layer and escaping free. It is true that *on the average* a number, equal to $30 \times 0{\cdot}20 = 6$ quanta will be absorbed by the rods, while the remaining 24 quanta will come through unchanged and be lost as far as vision is concerned (being absorbed in the black pigment behind the layer of rods, and eventually transformed into heat). The number 6 is an average number, because there is only *a certain probability*, equal to 0·20, of any one of the quanta being absorbed. To take an extreme case, it might happen by chance that all 30 quanta got through the rods, none being absorbed by them. Since each of the quanta has a probability equal to $4/5$ of not being absorbed, and these probabilities are independent of one another, the probability of all 30 quanta passing through is obtained simply by taking the product of all the probabilities relating to each quantum separately. This product is $(4/5)^{30}$; this is a small but finite number. It is also possible, but improbable, that all 30 might be absorbed; the probability here is $(1/5)^{30}$. The actual number of quanta absorbed, in other words, may vary each time. It may have any value between 0 and 30. The value 6 represents simply the mean of the numbers actually absorbed in a large number of trials.

This example is analogous to the tossing of a number of coins all at the same time. If one goes on tossing for a long time, it will be found that the number of heads obtained in a toss of, say, 10 coins, will *on the average* be $10 \times 0{\cdot}5 = 5$, because the chance of any one coin coming up heads is one in two. But the actual number of heads in each toss may be any one of the numbers 0, 1, 2, 3, 4, 5, 6, 7, 8, 9, 10—the number 5 occurring most frequently.

SOME PROPERTIES OF QUANTUM FLUCTUATIONS

The above example is enough to show that the number of quanta exciting the retina is bound to vary even when all conditions are kept rigorously constant. It is a fundamental law of quantum physics that *every absorption or emission of radiation can be traced down to individual processes in each of which a quantum of energy is exchanged.* The preceding result is due to this law in so far as it refers to absorption. It can be shown on similar grounds that it is also impossible to set up a source of light emitting a constant number of quanta in a constant period of time. It is, therefore, impossible to cause a constant number of 30 quanta to reach the retina in each trial, as assumed in the above argument. But this only emphasises still more the variability of the number of quanta absorbed by the retina, which this argument was precisely designed to demonstrate.

Referring again to the simile of the slot machine, such a variability would mean that it would be impossible to insert always exactly 6 pennies in the slot. Sometimes the number inserted would be 6, sometimes 7 or more, sometimes 5 or less, sometimes even 0.

If a large number of quanta is involved in emission or absorption, the variability of this number *on a percentage basis* will be less than in the case of a smaller number of quanta. In a similar way, if 1,000 coins are used in the tossing experiment above instead of 10, tosses giving numbers of heads differing widely from 50 per cent. will occur relatively less frequently than when 10 coins only are tossed each time.

A powerful source of light emits very large numbers of quanta. The number of quanta emitted in unit time, that is, the intensity of the source, can therefore have a very high degree of constancy on a percentage basis—the deviation from the mean intensity being expressed as a fraction of the mean, and not in absolute units such, for instance, as quanta. The use of an intense light source, however, would be of no avail in attempts to deliver constant small numbers of quanta to the retina, because the intensity would have to be cut down by absorbing a large proportion of the light on its way to the eye: the variability would then reappear for the same reasons as were given above.

In fact the variability, under constant experimental conditions, of the number of quanta absorbed by the retina depends only upon the average, or nominal, number of quanta absorbed. It does not depend on what occurs to the light before it is absorbed. Moreover, for any given nominal number—which, being an average, can be fractional—the actual number may be 0, or 1, or 2, or 3, or any other integer. There is no upper limit to the value of the actual number, but the probability of its being very much larger than the nominal number becomes very small. Actual numbers of quanta much higher than the average number are not impossible because, among other reasons, the source of light may suddenly emit by chance many more quanta than the average. On the other hand, it is always possible that the actual number may be zero, because as has been seen, the quanta reaching the retina may all fail to be absorbed. These *fluctuations* in the number of quanta are ultimately due to the fact that the emission or absorption of light occurs in individual independent quantum processes. *Only the probability of occurrence of a process remains constant under constant experimental conditions.*

FREQUENCY-OF-SEEING CURVES

On account of the existence of quantum fluctuations, the assumption that the retinal threshold n is subjected to wide variations ceases to be the only possible explanation of the experimental fact that under rigorously controlled and constant experimental conditions, the subject sometimes sees the light and sometimes fails to do so. Such behaviour must now be expected on purely physical grounds, even if the eye and the organism constituted a perfectly stable instrument for the detection of light.

For any value of the nominal average number of quanta absorbed by the retina, the actual number fluctuates, being any integer from zero upwards. An equation, formulated by the mathematician Poisson, applies in the present case and gives, in terms of the nominal number a alone, the probability that the actual number will be any number x chosen for consideration. This probability is equal to $a^x/e^a x!$. When the nominal number a is 6, for instance, the probability that the actual number x will be 0, 1, 2, 3, 4, or 5, is at once obtained using the Poisson formula. The sum of these various probabilities is the probability of the actual number being less than 6. If this composite probability is then subtracted from unity, the probability that the actual number will be 6 or more when the nominal number is 6, is obtained. This probability is thus found to be about 0·55. Thus if the retinal threshold n of the subject is constantly equal to 6 and if constant conditions, chosen so that the retina absorbs on the average 6 quanta, are maintained, the subject will see the light in about 55 per cent. of the trials and he will fail to see it in about 45 per cent.—even though his retinal threshold n, or his sensitivity to light, is assumed to be invariable.

For any other value of the nominal number, the probability of 6 quanta or more being absorbed can be calculated in the same way. When these probability values are plotted against the corresponding nominal numbers, a curve is obtained showing how the probability of seeing the light must vary with the light intensity, if the assumptions made in the theory are correct. The curve marked 6 in Fig. 54 has been calculated in this way. Its ordinate is the probability of 6 or more quanta being absorbed; its abscissa is the logarithm of the nominal number of quanta absorbed. (The logarithmic scale is used for reasons which will be apparent later.) For the nominal numbers smaller than 1·5 (1·5 corresponding to 0·18 on the abscissa scale, in log units), the probability is almost zero. As the nominal number increases above this value, the probability increases rapidly, reaching almost unity (or 100 per cent.) for a nominal number equal to 15 (corresponding to 1·18 on the abscissa scale). It will thus be noted that, according to the theory, practical certainty of seeing is not attained immediately on passing the threshold (6 quanta), but at a nominal value (15 quanta) far in excess of this.

In calculating the curve just considered it was assumed all through that the retinal threshold was $n = 6$. Similar curves corresponding to different values of n can be calculated in the same way. They are given in Fig. 54 for n varying from 1 to 9. As the number n increases the curve is displaced as a whole towards higher abscissae values, as one might expect. The intermediate S-shaped region of the curve also becomes steeper, that is, the region of transition, in which it is very

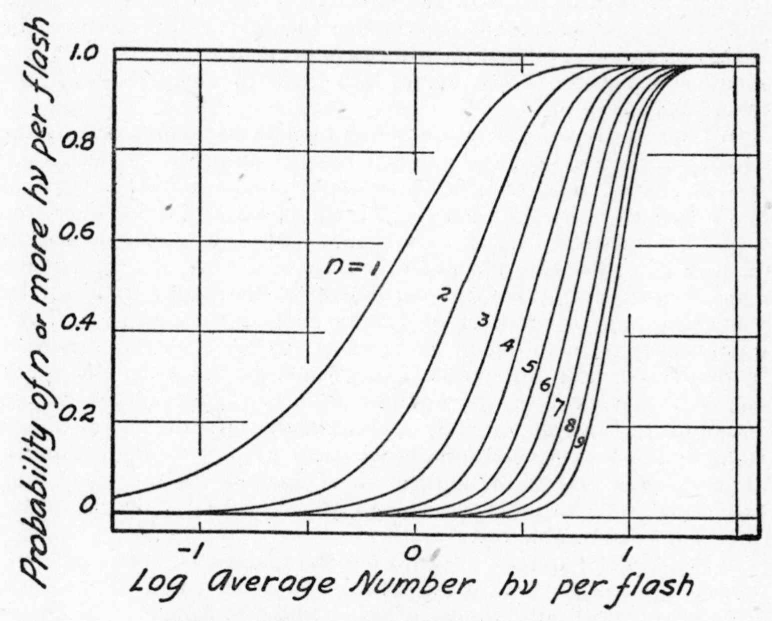

Fig. 54. Poisson probability distributions.

For any average or nominal number a of quanta ($h\nu$) per flash, the ordinates give the probabilities that the flash will deliver to the retina n or more quanta, depending on the value assumed for n. See text.

(From Hecht, Schlaer and Pirenne (1), *J. Gen. Physiol*, **25**, 819, 1942.)

uncertain whether the light will be seen or not at any one trial, becomes smaller in extent. (If there were no quantum fluctuations these S-shaped curves of course would each be replaced by vertical lines at the particular value of the abscissa corresponding to the retinal threshold, the probability of seeing jumping from zero to unity along this line.)

COMPARISON OF EXPERIMENTAL AND THEORETICAL CURVES

For a given subject at one sitting it is possible to determine experimentally, point by point, the curves giving the frequency with which the light is seen in terms of the intensity of the flash. Very special precautions are taken while determining such curves; for instance, the flashes of various nominal intensities are presented to the subject in a random sequence. These curves can them be compared with the theoretical curves of Fig. 54.

In order to do so, only the nominal number of quanta striking the cornea in the trial, not the nominal number absorbed by the retina, need be known. The frequency curves are plotted against the logarithm of the flash intensity and their shape is compared with the shape of the theoretical curves of Fig. 54. The shape of these curves is independent of the kind of intensity units used because of the use of a logarithmic scale; neither does the shape depend upon the (constant) factor by which the nominal number of quanta striking the cornea must be multiplied in order to obtain the nominal number of quanta absorbed by the retina. For multiplication of all intensity values by a constant factor is equivalent to the addition of a constant quantity to the values on the logarithmic scale. This merely shifts the curves bodily along this scale. Uncertainties in the calculation of the light losses in the eye media and of the absorption of light by the rods may thus be ignored, and an independent estimate of the value of the retinal threshold n can be obtained.

In Fig. 55 the frequency-of-seeing curves obtained with three different subjects are compared with theoretical curves calculated on the basis of purely physical fluctuations, as has just been explained. The circles represent the measurements, and the continuous lines the probability curves calculated for retinal thresholds of $n = 6$, $n = 7$, and $n = 5$ respectively. The shape of these particular theoretical curves agrees well with that of the experimental curves.

It may be concluded that, if the retinal threshold n was constant in each of the experiments, as assumed in the calculation of the curves, the retinal threshold n then had respectively the values 6, 7 and 5 for the three different subjects.

This determination of n is obtained using only the shape of the frequency curves without having regard to the scale of light intensities. In the preceding chapters, on the other hand, this scale has been taken into consideration, and it has been determined independently that the retinal threshold n has values ranging from 5 to 14 quanta. The agreement between these direct determinations and the values derived from the shape of the curves (n being assumed to be constant) can be considered satisfactory.

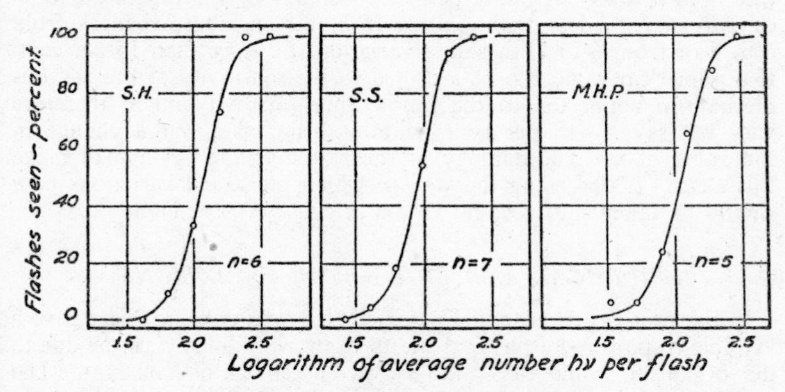

Fig. 55. Frequency-of-seeing curves.

Relation between the average energy content of a flash of light (in number of $h\nu$) and the frequency with which it is seen by three observers. Each point corresponds to 50 flashes. The curves are the Poisson distributions of Fig. 54 for values of n equal to 5, 6, and 7. See text.

(From Hecht, Schlaer and Pirenne (1), *J. Gen. Physiol.*, **25**, 819, 1942.)

Suppose the frequency-of-seeing curve of a particular subject in a given experiment has a shape corresponding to $n = 6$. Suppose, secondly, that it could be accurately established by the direct method that in the same experiment the average number of quanta absorbed by the retina at the threshold was also equal to 6. It would then be definitely proved that the retinal threshold n was constant and equal to 6 in this experiment, and that the uncertainty of seeing the light was entirely due to physical fluctuations. However, the direct determination of the number of quanta absorbed by a living retina is unfortunately complicated by unavoidable uncertainties. It cannot therefore be established with certainty whether or not n remains constant during one of these experiments, and whether or not the physical fluctuations are the *sole* cause of the observed frequency-of-seeing curves. The agreement between the two independent determinations of *n* is, however, sufficiently accurate to prove that the physical fluctuations are of very considerable magnitude, and play a major rôle in the experiments (5).

It may be worth pointing out here that constancy of the retinal threshold *n* does not imply perfect constancy of the organism, for *n* cannot vary by less than unity. If *n*, for instance, changes from 6 to 5 or from 6 to 7, these are variations of more than 15 per cent. If a numerical value can be ascribed to the sensitivity of the nervous mechanism connected to the retina, this sensitivity might therefore vary by, say, $\pm$ 15 per cent. without bringing about a change in the value of *n*. The analogy of the slot machine again may make this clear. (Concerning the way in which biological variations of *n* should be taken into account in the calculations, see (1).)

PHYSICAL AND BIOLOGICAL VARIATIONS

In the past it was generally assumed that when an organism gave a variable response to a physical stimulus, the variability must be due to the organism, while the stimulus was taken to be constant. The present results, on the other hand, show that in the case discussed the organism may possibly be constant, while the physical stimulus certainly undergoes wide and unavoidable fluctuations.

The meaning and implications of this should, perhaps, be somewhat elaborated. If the experiments gave very sharp frequency-of-seeing curves, rising abruptly from zero to unity probability at a particular intensity, the conclusion that the sensitivity of the threshold of the subject remained almost constant during the experiment would probably not be questioned. Now the crux of the present argument is that, considering the small quantities of light involved, the very possibility of such abrupt curves must be rejected, precisely because of the quantum properties of light, even if, in an ideal situation, a given retina were demonstrably constant. Furthermore, although these curves, from the point of view of a continuum theory of light, admittedly appear very shallow, they could, according to the quantum theory, scarcely be steeper than in fact they are. The constancy of the organism's sensitivity is borne out just as much by these shallow curves as it would be by more abrupt curves if a continuum theory of light were true. One must accept these considerable physical fluctuations or else reject the theories of quantum physics.

Fluctuation phenomena are very important throughout modern physics. They are observed in the case of electrons, α-particles, molecules, as well as quanta (although, in the case of quanta of visible light, there does not appear to be any exact parallel to the case of human vision, but neither is there found an instrument with the sensitivity of the human eye). In the case of electrons, the emission fluctuations in radio-valves cause the irreducible " thermal noise " which sets a natural limit to the efficiency of electrical amplifying systems. On account of the very high sensitivity of the eye, it is therefore not surprising that one should find quantum fluctuations operative in its behaviour in certain circumstances.

According to the quantum theory, only the probability of seeing a light can be known. Whether or not the light will actually be seen in a particular trial (at a point of the S-shaped part of the frequency curve), it is impossible to predict. That is why statistical data must be obtained from the experiments, which because of this, are long and difficult. But the fact that one is dealing only with probabilities does not impair the efficiency of experimentation or prediction. One might recall the well-known epigram: while there are few things less certain than the date of a given person's death, there are few things more certain than the profits of life insurance companies.

BIBLIOGRAPHY AND NOTES

Details and bibliography relating to the matters discussed in this and the two preceding chapters will be found in:

(1) HECHT, S., SHLAER, S., and PIRENNE, M. H. (1942). "Energy, Quanta, and Vision," *J. General Physiology*, **25**, 819-840.

(2) STILES, W. S. (1944). "Current Problems of Visual Research." *Proc. Physical Soc. London*, **56**, 329-356. Includes report of a discussion.

See also the following papers, according to which 2 quanta absorbed by the retina would be enough to produce a threshold stimulation:

(3) BOUMAN, M. A., and VAN DER VELDEN, H. A. (1947). *J. Opt. Soc. Amer.*, **37**, 908-919.

(4) BAUMGARDT, E. (1948). *J. General Physiology*, **31**, 269-290.

(5) It may be noted that when conditions are not carefully controlled, e.g. when the observer is untrained, or tired, much shallower frequency-of-seeing curves are obtained: then large biological variations certainly occur.

Chapter IX

THE EYES AND THE VISION OF INSECTS

THE STRUCTURE OF COMPOUND EYES

The eyes of insects are constructed in quite a different way from those of vertebrates. It has been possible to determine by experiments the visual acuity of insects such as the honey-bee at various light intensities, and to correlate these data with the anatomical data of the insect eye. When the scale of magnitude is disregarded, these results have great similarity to those concerning human vision. Thus, fundamentally similar performance is achieved in man and in insects by the use of visual organs of very different structures, and some basic resemblance in the mechanism may be expected in both cases.

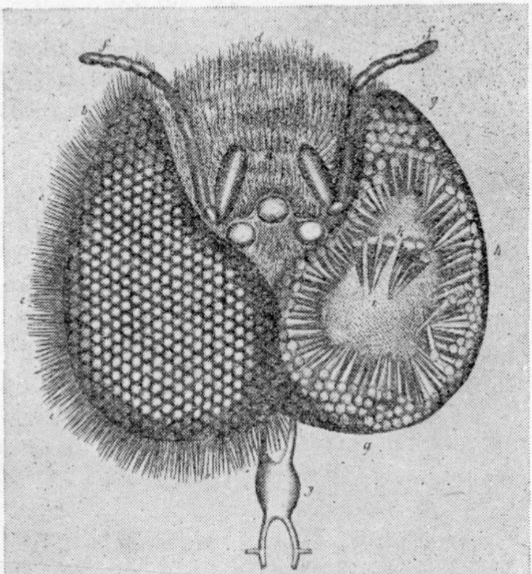

Fig. 56. The eyes of the honey-bee, according to an ancient drawing. Explanation in text.

(From Swammerdam (1), *Bybel der Natuure, Leyden,* 1737. Reproduced by permission of Cambridge University Library.)

Fig. 56 reproduces an old anatomical drawing of the eyes of the honey bee. Although inaccurate in details, the drawing shows on the left the surface of the intact eye with its numerous hexagonal facets, and on the right, inside the dissected eye, the conical elements each of which corresponds to one of the facets of the cornea, that is, of the transparent horny layer forming the surface of the eye.

Fig. 57 is a modern drawing showing in detail a section of two of the thousands of elements and facets forming the eye of the bee. Fig. 58 is a section, drawn at a lower magnification, of the eye of the cockchafer. Each of the elements forming these compound eyes is called an *ommatidium*.

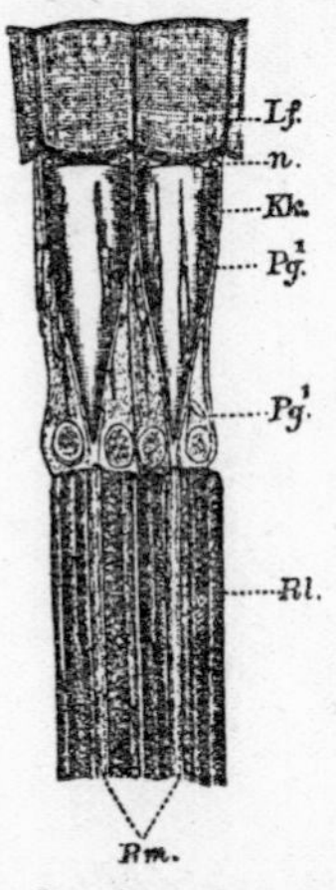

Fig. 57. Section showing two separate ommatidia of the faceted eye of a honey-bee.

Lf cornea, showing two facets.
Kk crystalline cone. (Such conical elements, which act only as dioptric apparatus, must not be confused with the photoreceptor cones of vertebrate retinae.)
Rl retinula. The retinulae are connected to the optic nerve.

(After Grenacher, in Lubbock (2), *On the Senses of Animals*, Kegan Paul, Trench, Trubner & Co. Ltd., London, 1899.)

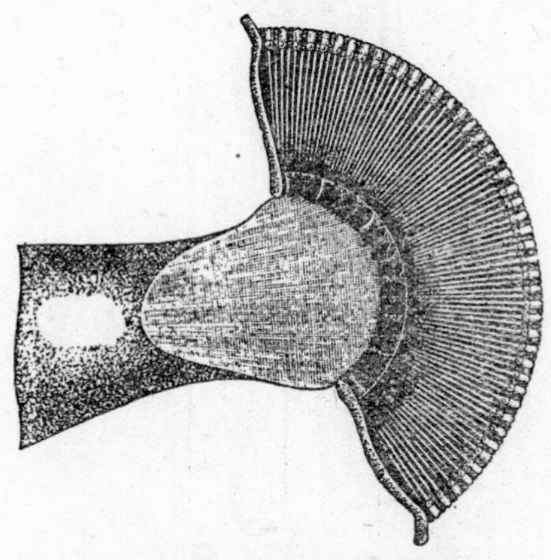

Fig. 58. Section through the eye of a cockchafer (Melolontha).

The drawing shows the regular radial arrangement of the ommatidia.

(After Strauss-Dürckheim in Lubbock (2), *On the Senses of Animals*, Kegan Paul, Trench, Trubner & Co. Ltd., London, 1899.)

The eyes of crustaceans are also built on the same pattern. Fig. 59 shows in detail two ommatidia from the eye of a crayfish. The eye of the king crab, which has been shown in section in Fig. 46 of Chapter V, is a primitive eye of the same type. The figure clearly shows five ommatidia, each connected to its own nerve fibres.

It is clear that eyes such as these are built on a plan entirely different from that of the human eye. Considered as a whole, the peripheral endings of all the nerve fibres in these eyes must form a light-sensitive

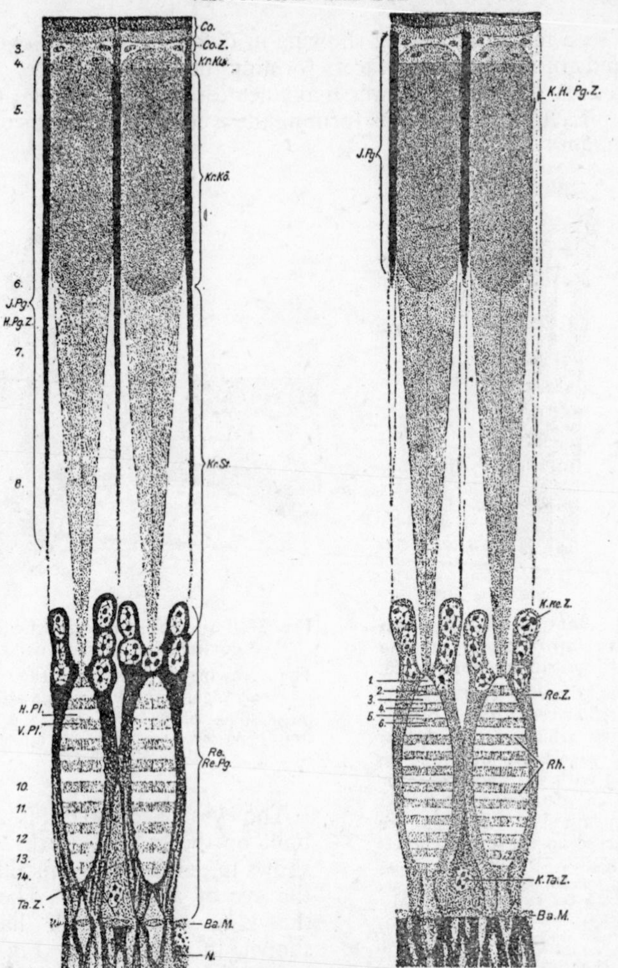

Fig. 59. Longitudinal section through two ommatidia of the crayfish, *Astacus fluviatilis*.

On the left: light-adapted eye. *On the right*: dark-adapted eye. Note that the black pigment migrates to different positions according to the state of adaptation of the eye. Cf. Fig. 63. *Co* cornea, *Re* retinula, *N* nerve fibre. The cornea and the crystalline cones *Kr* are transparent in the living animal. High magnification. (After Bernhards (12), *Z. Zool.*, **116**, 649, 1916.)

surface similar to the mosaic of rods and cones of the human retina. But the retina in this case is convex, rather than concave as in the human eye. Unlike the vertebrate retina, it does not cover the walls of a camera obscura, on to which an optical system projects an inverted picture of the outside world. In fact, as will appear presently, the structure of these eyes is such that the sensitive element of each ommatidium receives light only from that part of the outside world exactly facing its facet. The result is that an erect image of the outside object is formed on the mosaic of nervous elements sensitive to light in the compound eye. This mode of vision was first expounded in 1826 by Johannes Müller (4). He had reached the conclusion on theoretical grounds that the existence of eyes of this type was possible, and subsequently found his theory verified by insect and crustacean eyes, whose mode of operation had remained unexplained until his day.

MODE OF OPERATION OF COMPOUND EYES

Suppose a visual organ, constituted simply by a small flat retina AB, as shown in Fig. 60, were exposed to the outside world without the

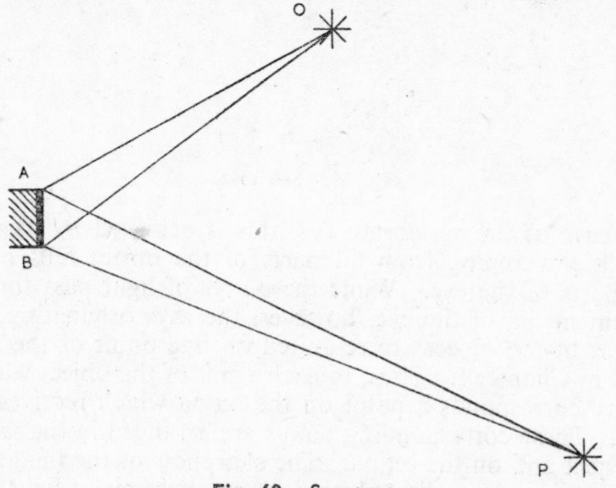

Fig. 60. See text.

intermediary of any lens or other apparatus. In such a retina, the only difference in the stimulation produced by different luminous objects will be one due to differences of general illumination of AB. Two light sources, O and P, placed in different positions relative to the retina, would each illuminate the whole sensitive surface AB in an almost even manner (provided none of the sources came extremely close to AB, in which case that part of the retina nearest to the source would be much more strongly illuminated than the rest). Accordingly, there would be in practice no essential difference between the illumination and stimulation produced by one or by several sources in any positions.

In order to have even the most rudimentary form-vision, some arrangement is demanded by which local variations of illumination consistently related to the position and brightness of the objects to be seen, are produced on the retinal mosaic.

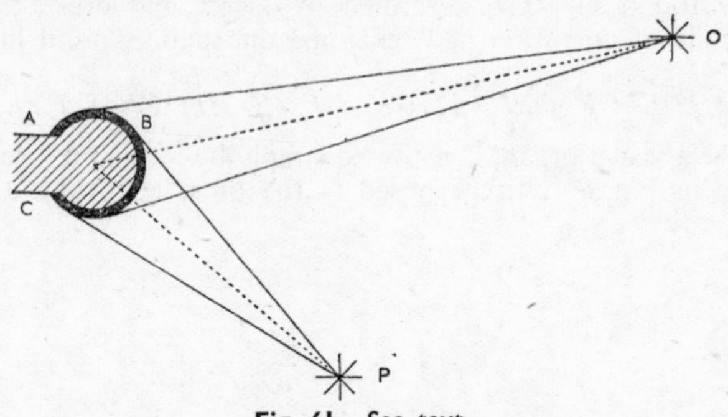

Fig. 61. See text.

In the case of the vertebrate eye, this is achieved by its refractive system. Light coming from all parts of the object falls on all the external parts of the eye. While these rays of light pass through the transparent media of the eye, however, the rays originating from the same point of the object are re-united on one point of the retina, as explained in Chapter I. Thus, to each point of the object which emits light, there corresponds a point on the retina which receives some of this light. These corresponding points are arranged in the same order on the object and on the retina. The sharpness of the image is determined by the accuracy with which such convergence of light on to the retina takes place.

We may now consider an imaginary visual organ, consisting of a spherical sensitive surface ABC, whose convex surface faces the outside world, as shown in Fig. 61. Unlike the case envisaged in Fig. 60, two different light sources O and P now produce two different patterns of stimulation on the retina ABC. The illumination produced by one source is uneven. It is at a maximum at that point of the spherical surface where the light from the source falls in the direction of the corresponding radius of the sphere. The illumination is zero at the diametrically opposite point. The half of the sphere surface around this point is in the shade. In the case of Fig. 61, two distinct regions of the retina are therefore illuminated by the two sources O and P.

The ommatidia of compound eyes are really a device interposed between the retina and the outside world, whose function it is to make such patterns of light intensity on a convex retina very much sharper.

The ommatidia are separated from one another by black pigment. In the simpler type of compound eyes, only the light entering an ommatidium in the direction of its axis can reach the nervous element sensitive to light at the tip of the ommatidium (Fig. 62). Light coming from a given point falls into a large number of ommatidia, but stimulates only the ommatidium whose axis lies in the direction of the source. The rays of light from the source which fall into other ommatidia at different angles, strike the black pigment between the ommatidia, and are lost by absorption, without inducing any nervous excitation. Thus, a given point of the retina only receives light from a corresponding point of the object, and light from a particular point of the object can stimulate only one or a few elements of the retinal mosaic. This result is achieved by a process of isolation, rather than convergence, of light. In this way, an erect image of the external objects is formed in compound eyes, at the level of the mosaic of light receptors.

Figs. 57 and 59 show that the anatomy of the elements of compound eyes can be very complicated. Moreover the transparent structures inside the ommatidia may have curious optical properties. A transparent cylinder, for instance, may concentrate and deflect light falling on its base, not by virtue of its shape, but because the substance in its centre is denser and refracts light more strongly than the substance forming its outer parts (5). Small inverted images of external objects can be formed at some level in certain ommatidia, but there is no retina to receive these images, as in a vertebrate eye. Insects, therefore, do not see, as was sometimes stated, by the use of " thousands of eyes " as if each ommatidium were a distinct " eye." On the contrary, the schema of Johannes Müller has been proved to represent essentially how the compound eye functions (2). This is true in spite of the fact that in some eyes, called *superposition eyes*, the layer of light-receptors

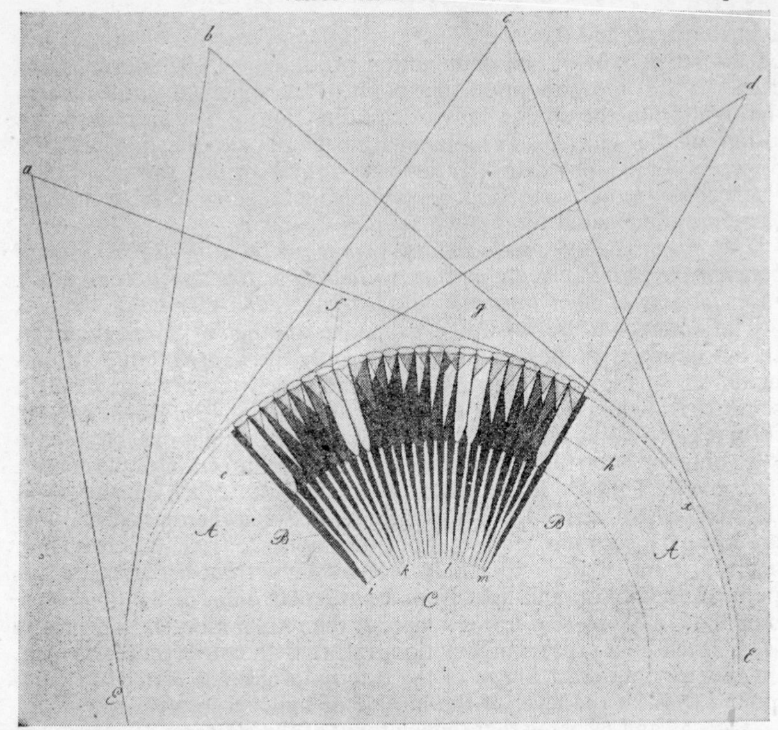

Fig. 62. Mode of operation of a compound eye according to Johannes Müller. Showing the distribution of light produced in it by four sources of light *a*, *b*, *c* and *d*.

EE represents the external surface of the eye with the facets of the transparent cornea.
AA represents the conical elements of the ommatidia, transparent in their centre but covered laterally with opaque pigment.
BB represents the optic nerve fibres in contact with the lower tips of the transparent cones. The endings of the fibres are sensitive to light.
C is the optic ganglion of the brain onto which the optic fibres converge.

When light emitted by the different points *abcd* falls on the eye, the transparent cone *h* is completely filled with light falling along its axis and coming from the source *d*. The ommatidia at the side of *h* receive light from *d*, but none of them is filled with light down to its tip, the light going less deeply the farther the ommatidium is from the line *md*. The optic fibre *m* corresponding to the cone *h* is thus excited by light emitted by the source *d*, while light of the same source *d* entering other ommatidia is unable to excite their nerve fibres, because it is absorbed by the black pigment separating the ommatidia. Similarly, light from *c* stimulates exclusively the two ommatidia *g l*; light from *b* the two ommatidia *f k*; and light from *a* the ommatidium *i*.

(After J. Müller (4), *Zur vergleichenden Physiologie des Gesichtssinnes*, Leipzig, 1826. Reproduced by permission of the Cambridge University Library.)

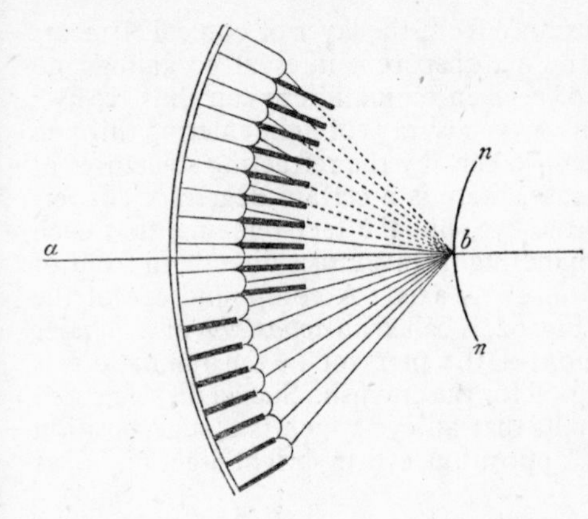

Fig. 63. Diagram showing the effect of the migration of the pigment in a compound eye. Cf. Fig. 59.

The axial ray of light is indicated by the line *ab*. In the lower part of the figure the pigment is in the position for dim light and the eye admits lateral rays (superposition eye). In the upper part it is in the position for bright light and the eye excludes lateral rays (apposition eye).

(After Exner (5), *Die Physiologie der Facettirten Augen*, F. Deuticke, Leipzig and Vienna, 1891.)

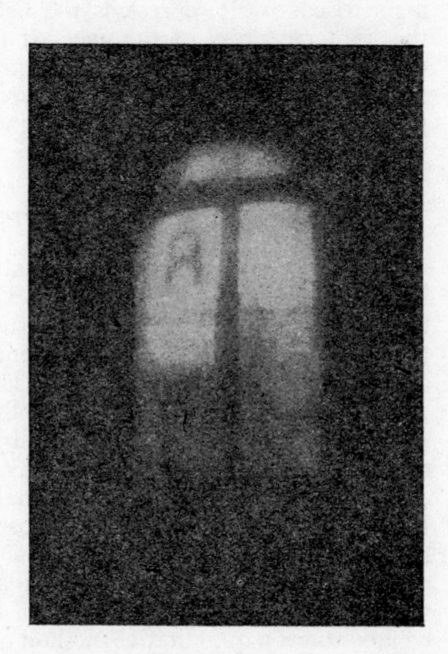

Fig. 64. The image formed in an insect eye.

Microphotograph, made by Exner, of the erect retinal image formed inside the eye of the firefly (Lampyris splendidula). Magnification 120. The image is that of a bow window, through which a church is seen. On one pane of the window a letter *R* cut out of black paper was pasted. The distance from the insect eye to the window was 225 centimeters ; to the church, 135 feet.

(After Exner (5), *Die Physiologie der Facettirten Augen*, F. Deuticke, Leipzig and Vienna, 1891.)

BB of Fig. 62 is placed at a distance from the layer of conical elements *AA*, being separated from it by a transparent interval containing no pigment. The light receptor of a given ommatidium can thus receive, besides the light falling along its own axis, rays of light entering through neighbouring ommatidia which are bent by the refracting structures of these ommatidia. In such a case, there is a certain degree of convergence of light, as in a vertebrate eye, but the fact remains, that each receptor receives only light originating from sources directly in front of its ommatidium in the direction of its axis. A compound eye of the simple type, corresponding to Fig. 62, is called an *apposition eye*. Under the influence of light, migration of the pigment in the ommatidia is found to occur, as shown in Fig. 59 for the crayfish. Such a displacement of pigment may have as a result, that an eye which is a superposition eye in dim light becomes an apposition eye in bright light (5, 3) as shown in Fig. 63.

Fig. 64 reproduces a photograph, taken by Exner, of the optical image formed by the superposition eye of the fire-fly, as seen through a microscope. It represents the light pattern formed at the level of the light receptors of the eye. It is evident that the discrimination of form by this insect cannot be finer than the accuracy of the details shown in this image—clearly no very high degree of accuracy. It is just about the visual acuity of a man seeing the same scene lit by the sky of a moonless night.

MEASUREMENT OF THE VISUAL ACUITY OF INSECTS

Something of the powers of visual discrimination by animals can be learnt from experiments. This is often done by using some form of training. For instance, an animal such as the honey-bee can be trained to come and take sugar from a container placed beside a black disc, and to avoid an empty container placed near a black cross. If, now, an empty container is placed beside both disc and cross, and the latter are moved about at random, the bee still makes for the disc. It follows that the bee can discriminate in some way between the disc and cross. Such experiments are susceptible of many variations and have yielded important results (6). It is also possible, however, to use more direct methods, eliminating the preliminary training process. One fruitful direct method is based on the fact that most animals with eyes respond to sudden movements in their visual field. This kind of behaviour can be used to get a quantitative method of measuring visual acuity. Hecht, one of the originators of this method, has stated (7) its fundamental notions as follows:

"If the visual field of a sensitive animal is made up of a pattern of dark and illuminated bars of equal size, the animal will respond to a displacement of this field only when it can distinguish the components of the pattern. In case the animal cannot resolve the black and white bars, the field will appear uniformly illuminated and displacement of the pattern will elicit no response. If visual acuity varies with illumination, then the capacity to respond to these movements in the visual field will depend on the illumination and on the size of the pattern. One can in this way determine the relation between the size of the bars in the visual pattern and the minimum illumination at which a movement of the pattern causes a response in the animal.

"The honey-bee is very sensitive to such changes in its visual field, and responds by a reflex sideways movement of the head and the thorax. If the bee is crawling, the response becomes evident by a sudden change in the direction of its progression, which is opposite in sign to the movement in the environmental pattern. It is an extraordinary sight to watch the precision with which a bee changes its direction of creeping under the conditions of these experiments. If the pattern is moved, say to the left, the creeping bee swings sharply to the right through an angle which is easily 45°, and may be much more, and continues creeping in the new direction. During a single crawl of perhaps ten centimetres, we have frequently made a bee alter its direction right and left by moving the pattern left and right as many as four or five times in rapid succession. The behaviour of the fruit fly, Drosophila, under similar circumstances, is even more dramatic. Drosophila confined in a long, narrow, rectangular glass cell, will crawl continuously from one end of the cell to the other. If the pattern of black and white bars which constitutes the visual field of the animal is moved in the same direction in which the animal is creeping steadily, it will stop sharply, turn around, and reverse its direction of creeping. By moving the bars back and forth, a Drosophila may be made to change its direction of creeping over and over again within a space of about one or two centimetres."*

Fig. 65 gives the results of experiments made in this way on the honey-bee. Visual acuity is defined as the reciprocal of the visual angle subtended by the smallest details which the eye can distinguish—in this case, the thickness of the black, or white, bars. This angle is expressed

* Quotation used by permission of the President and Fellows of Harvard College.

in minutes of arc, so that if the thickness of the bars which is distinguished corresponds to an angle of 1 minute, the visual acuity is unity; if it corresponds to, say, 60 minutes, the visual acuity is 1/60.

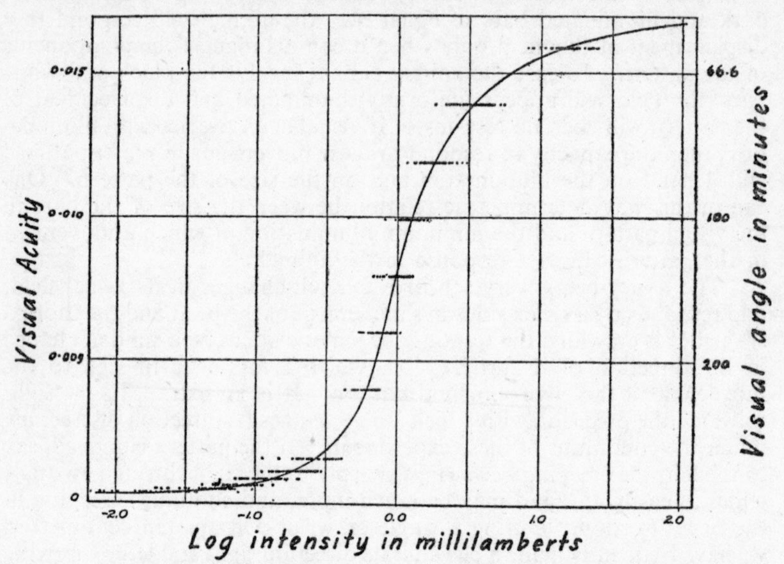

Fig. 65. Relation between visual acuity and illumination in the honey-bee. See text. Each dot represents a single measurement with a single bee. The curve is drawn through the mean values of the measurements.
(After Hecht and Wolf (8), *J. Gen. Physiol.*, **12**, 727, 1929.)

THE MAXIMUM ACUITY OF THE BEE

Fig. 65 shows that the maximum acuity of the bee in bright light is about 0·017, which corresponds to a visual angle 1/0·017 = 59 minutes, that is, about 1°. This acuity corresponds approximately to a pattern made of white and black bars as thick as those of Fig. 66, seen from a distance of 50 cm. The bee is just able to resolve such a pattern at this distance; it fails to respond to movements of a pattern made of thinner bars. This makes it evident that the resolving power of the eye of the bee is very considerably less than that of the human eye. This low acuity of insect vision is in keeping with the indistinctness of the retinal image formed by the eye of the fire-fly, shown in Fig. 64.

In order that the patterns of black and white be resolved, it is necessary that when a black bar is in the direction of the axis of an ommatidium, the white bar next to it be in front of the adjacent ommatidium, and so forth. If the bars are thin enough for a black bar and a white bar to be both in front of the same ommatidium, the amounts of light falling into successive neighbouring ommatidia are all equal. The stimulation is thus the same as if the pattern were replaced by a uniform grey pattern, and so the eye is naturally incapable of resolving the pattern. The determining factor for visual acuity is therefore the angle between the axes of adjacent ommatidia—not the dimensions as such of the ommatidia. The smallest angles between the axes of adjacent ommatidia in the honey-bee have been found equal to 0·9 or 1° (Fig. 67). The maximum acuity of which the eye of the bee is capable thus agrees well with its anatomical structure. The acuity of the fly Drosophila has been found to be 0·0018; that is, about ten times smaller than that of the bee (10). This corresponds to the pattern of Fig. 66 seen from a distance of 5 cm. The ommatidial angle in this case is 4·2°, while the resolving power corresponds to an angle twice as large. This discrepancy may be due to the small total number of ommatidia contained in the very inefficient eye of Drosophila.

Fig. 66.

Fig. 68 shows how the resolving power of a mosaic of elements decreases as the size of the elements increases. It represents the geometrical image of black-and-white test objects (I), together with the corresponding patterns produced on three imaginary retinal mosaics of increasing coarseness (II, III and IV). It will be noted that something of the vertical single line remains noticeable even where the grating of black lines (of the same thickness as the vertical line) has become a uniform grey. In order that a single line be noticed, it is only necessary that a single row of elements be stimulated to a different degree from the other elements, while in order to resolve a grating, each row of elements must be stimulated more or less than its neighbouring rows. For this reason, the size of the elements is a limiting factor for the

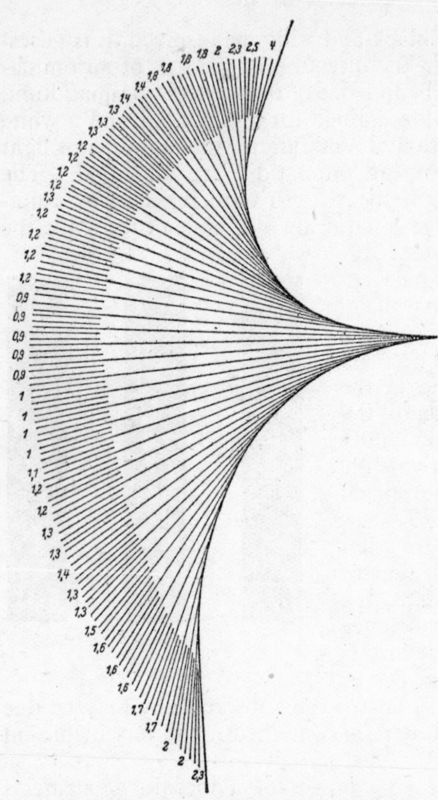

Fig. 67.

Vertical section through the eye of the honey-bee.

The drawing shows the way in which the angular separation of adjacent ommatidia varies in different parts of the eye ; the value of the angles is given in degrees. The ommatidia are drawn in groups of three.

(After Baumgärtner (9), *Z. vergl. Physiol.*, **7**, 56, 1928.)

grating, while it is not for the single line. In the case of the honey-bee, it has also been found that a single black bar can be resolved even when it subtends an angle which is only one quarter of a degree, that is, one quarter of the angle between two ommatidia (11).

VARIATION OF ACUITY WITH LIGHT INTENSITY IN THE BEE

In Fig. 65 the abscissa represents the logarithm of the brightness of the white bars of the pattern, while the ordinate represents the visual acuity of the bee for each brightness. At a low brightness such as 0·02 millilambert, the acuity is only 0·0003. This corresponds to the

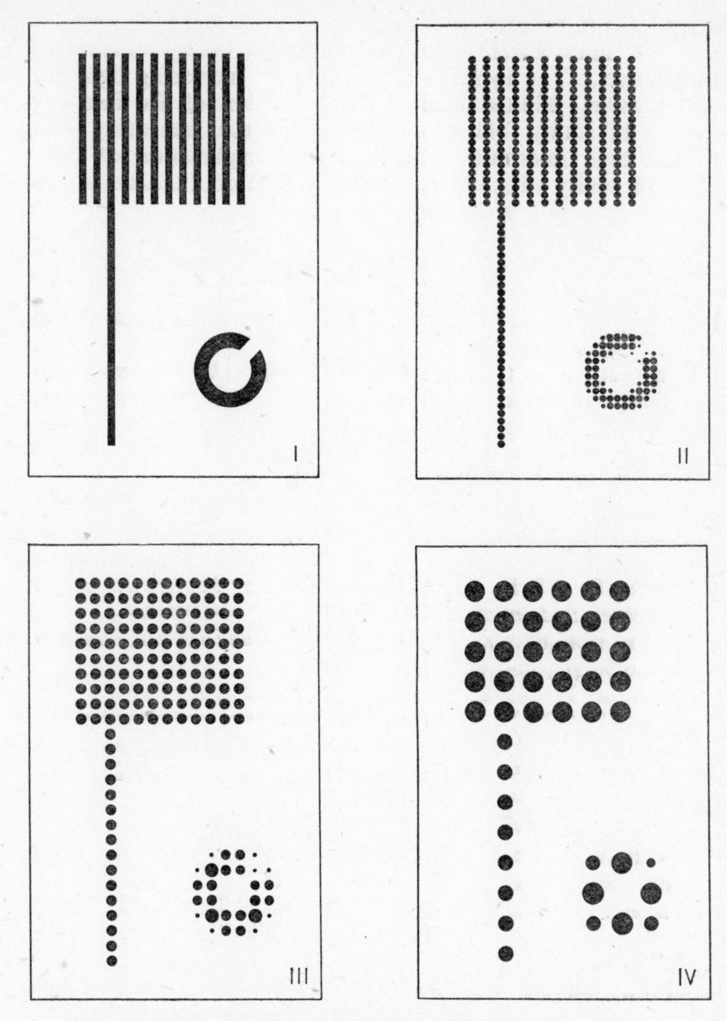

Fig. 68. Resolving power of three different mosaics.
See p. 107.

pattern of Fig. 66 seen at a distance of only one centimetre, and is about 50 times lower than the maximum acuity obtained at 15 millilamberts. The increase of acuity with increasing light-intensity is progressive. Plotted against the logarithm of the intensity, the variation of acuity follows an S-shaped curve, increasing slowly at low and high intensities. The complete explanation of this large change of acuity with intensity remains one of the aims of research in the mechanisms of vision.

BIBLIOGRAPHY

(1) SWAMMERDAM, J. (1737–38). *Bybel der Natuure* (in Dutch and Latin), Leyden.

(2) LUBBOCK, Sir J. (Lord Avebury) (1899). *On the senses, instincts, and intelligence of animals, with special reference to insects*, 292 pp., London.

(3) PARKER, G. H. (1932). "The Movements of the retinal pigment," *Ergebnisse der Biologie*, **9**, 239–291.

(4) MÜLLER, J. (1826). *Zur vergleichenden Physiologie des Gesichtssinnes des Menschen und der Thiere, nebst einen Versuch über die Bewegungen der Augen und über den menschlichen Blick*, Leipzig.

(5) EXNER, S. (1891). *Die Physiologie der Facettirten Augen von Krebsen und Insecten*, 206 pp., Leipzig and Vienna.

(6) See: BUDDENBROCK, W. V. (1937). *Grundriss der vergleichenden Physiologie*, 2nd ed.; 2 vol., Berlin.
PIÉRON, H. (1941). *Psychologie Zoologique*, Paris.

(7) HECHT, S. (1931). "The Retinal Processes concerned with visual acuity and color vision," *Bulletin No.* 4 *of the Howe Laboratory of Ophthalmology*, Harvard Medical School, Cambridge, Mass.

(8) HECHT, S., and WOLF, E. (1929). "The visual acuity of the honey-bee," *J. Gen. Physiol.*, **12**, 727.

(9) BAUMGÄRTNER, H. (1928). "Der Formensinn und die Sehschärfe der Bienen," *Z. vergl. Physiol.*, **7**, 56.

(10) HECHT, S., and WALD, G. (1934). "The visual acuity and intensity discrimination of Drosophila," *J. Gen. Physiol.*, **17**, 517–547.

(11) BUDDENBROCK, W. V. (1935). "Versuche über die Wahrnehmungsgrenze des Insektenauges," *Naturwissenschaften*, **23**, 154.

(12) BERNHARDS, H. (1916). "Der Bau des Komplexauges von *Astacus fluviatilis*," *Z. Zool.*, **116**, 649–707.

Chapter X

VISUAL ACUITY OF MAN

SOME EXPERIMENTAL DATA

THE relation between visual acuity and light intensity in man is shown in Fig. 69, plotted as the same relation is plotted for the honey-bee in Fig. 65. Here also the variation of acuity with the logarithm of intensity is represented by an S-shaped curve. The range of intensity corresponding to the steep part of the curve is larger in the case of man, but the main difference between the curve for man and the curve for the bee is in the scale of acuity values. The maximum human acuity, at high intensities, is found to be between 1·5 and 2. This is 100 times higher than the acuity of the bee, and 1,000 times higher than that of Drosophila. It corresponds to a pattern made of bars such as that of Fig. 66 seen from a distance of 50 metres, as against 50 centimetres for the bee, and 5 centimetres for Drosophila. Notwithstanding these considerable differences in the absolute values, there is a striking similarity in the way acuity varies with intensity in all three cases.

The lowest values recorded in Fig. 69 for human acuity, about 0·03, are not the lowest which can be measured. Human acuity continues to decrease as intensity decreases. Before the light becomes altogether invisible, that is before the absolute threshold is reached, acuity values as low as those of insects are reached. It must be noted that as long as some light is seen, some vision of form remains. In the darkest moonless nights, for instance, when the sky is evenly blanketed by thick clouds, it is usually possible to distinguish the sky from the ground, because it appears brighter. Any such spatial discrimination necessitates form vision, and may be said to correspond to a certain, very low, degree of visual acuity.

Variations of acuity in figures such as Fig. 69 and Fig. 65, are not clearly shown for the lowest values of the acuity scale. This is because this scale is a linear one. By plotting the logarithm of the acuity against the logarithm of the intensity, the changes in the smaller values can be made clearer. Fig. 70 is plotted in this way. It represents visual acuity measured using blue light and red light instead of white light as in the preceding experiments. The value of the maximum acuity reached at high intensities is practically the same for red and for blue light; it is

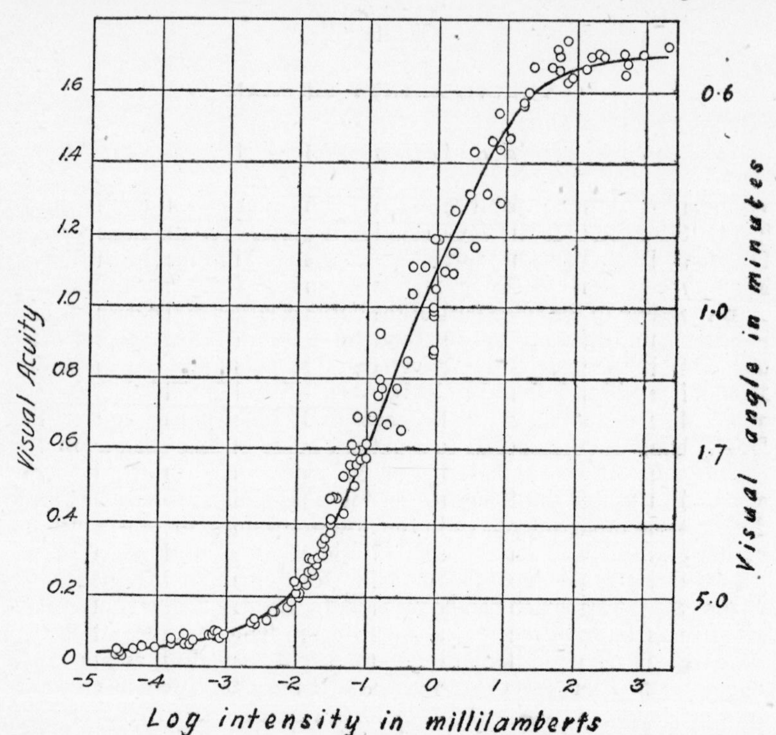

Fig. 69. Relation between human visual acuity and illumination in white light.

The circles represent measurements by König, replotted by Hecht. See text.
(After Hecht (1), *Bull. No. 4 of the Howe Laboratory of Ophthalmology*, 1931. Reproduced by permission of the President and Fellows of Harvard College.)

also the same when white light is used. At low intensities the shape of the curve is quite different for red and for blue light. This is related to the Purkinje phenomenon. The rods, being more sensitive to blue than the cones, function alone at low intensities of blue light and a separate part of the curve refers to them. This does not occur with red light since the sensitivity of both rods and cones to this kind of light is much the same. The curve for red is thus a continuous curve, showing no rod component at low intensities.

In experiments of this nature, the lighting is continuous, and the subject uses his eye in a normal way. The region of the retina used is not always the same; at high intensities, for instance, the fovea is always used, whereas at very low intensities, the subject may use the

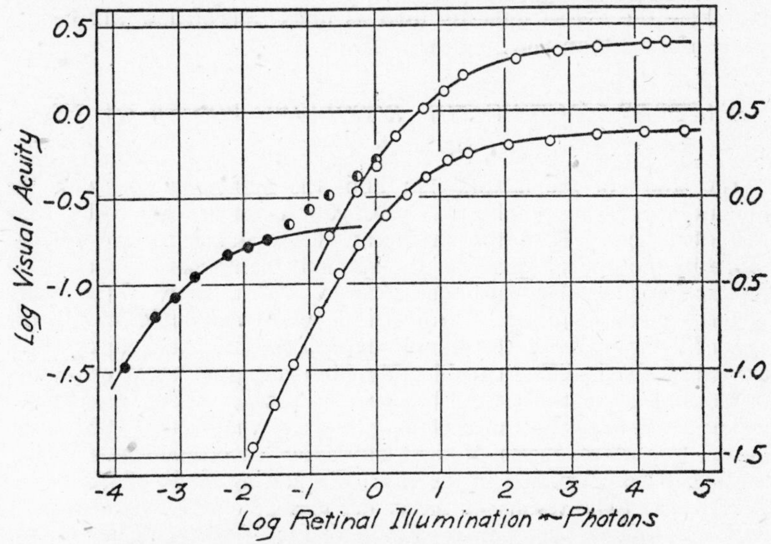

Fig. 70. Human visual acuity in red and blue light.

The test object here is not a grating but a broken ring, similar to the C in Fig. 68 I. The lower data (ordinates at the right) were obtained using light from the red end, the upper data (ordinates at the left) using light from the blue end of the spectrum. The filled circles represent the measurements made with the retinal periphery in a subjectively colourless field and correspond to rod vision. The half-filled circles are the measurements made with the parafovea in a subjectively coloured field and probably represent combined rod and cone vision. All other circles are measurements made with the fovea and represent pure cone vision.

(" Photons " here are special units of retinal illumination, not to be confused with the photons of quantum theory.)

(From Shlaer, Smith and Chase (2), *J. Gen. Physiol.*, **25**, 553, 1942.)

periphery. At some intermediate intensities of blue light the subject may use either the fovea or the parafovea. In this last case, his acuity, at a certain intensity, will be higher if he uses the parafovea: the reason being, apparently, that in parafoveal vision both rods and cones function together (2). When white light is used, the results, if they are plotted in the same manner as Fig. 70, will again show a division in the cone curve and the rod curve, as they did for blue light, but to a less marked extent (3).

The considerable range over which the eye can function should again be noted in Fig. 70. It covers more than 8 logarithmic units; that is, taking the lowest intensity used as unity, the highest will have a value of more than one hundred millions.

FACTORS LIMITING THE RESOLVING POWER OF THE HUMAN EYE

The study of the factors that limit the maximum acuity of the human eye is a complicated investigation which cannot be fully presented here. Both the sharpness of the image formed on the retina by the optical system of the eye, and the fineness of the retinal mosaic must be taken into consideration. In the study of the acuity of the bee consideration of geometrical optics were sufficient. In the case of the human eye, the retinal image of the finest test object which can be resolved, differs considerably from the geometrical projection of the object on the retina, because the details of this geometrical image come near the order of magnitude of the wave-length of the light. Important effects of light diffraction accordingly take place. These can be calculated in the case of a grating made of black and white bars. (The results of the acuity measurements obtained using such a grating are very similar to those of Fig. 70 where a C test-object was used.) The full line of Fig. 71 represents the distribution of light intensity across the retinal image of such a grating. The geometrical image would be represented by the dotted line, in which the light intensity jumps abruptly from zero to full intensity on passing from a black to a white bar. Instead of such an image, diffraction phenomena produce the intensity distribution shown by the sinusoidal full line, oscillating around the 50 per cent. level of intensity. The maxima of intensity corresponding to the centre of the image of the white bars reach only 61 per cent., and the minima go down to only 39 per cent., instead of 100 and zero as in the geometrical image.

Acuity, then, may be limited by two distinct factors. A fine grating may remain unresolved either because the darker and brighter bars of its image do not fall on different rows of cones in the retina, or because the difference between the maxima and the minima intensities in its blurred retinal image is too small to be detected by neighbouring rows of cones. The second possibility can be ruled out by experiments using

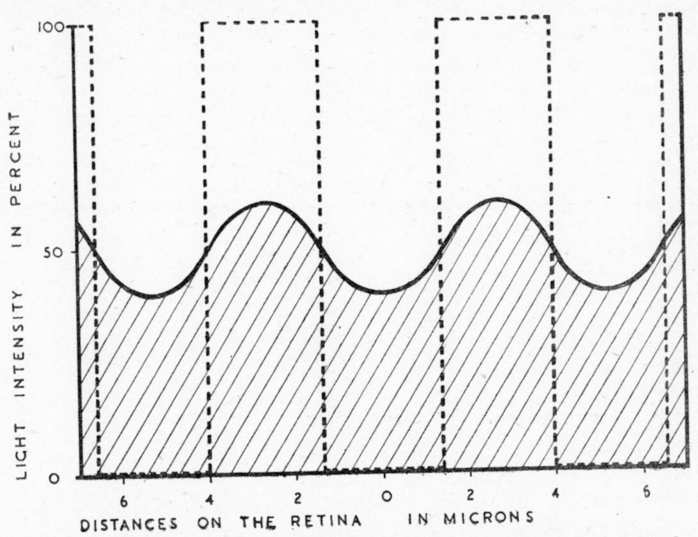

Fig. 71. Retinal image of a grating which can just be resolved.
The distribution of light in the retinal image of a grating corresponding to a visual acuity of 1.7, calculated taking diffraction and chromatic aberration into account. See text.
(After Shlaer (3), *J. Gen. Physiol.*, **21**, 165, 1937.)

a grating having the same number of bars per centimetre as the first, but limiting the width of the black bars to one half of their width in the first grating. The difference between the intensity maxima and minima in the retinal image of the new grating is now half that of the first, and yet the eye resolves it as well. It appears, therefore, that it is the first factor, namely, the dimension of the cones, which sets the limit of acuity in the case of the grating (3). The distance between the centre of the retinal image of a black bar and that of the image of an adjacent white bar is 2 to 2·5 microns. Anatomical investigations give very similar values for the distance between the centres of adjacent cones in the middle of the fovea centralis (3, 4) (cf. Chapter II).

VISIBILITY OF SINGLE BLACK LINES

It has been seen that the bee is able to detect a black bar subtending a visual angle of one-quarter of a degree, equal to only one-fourth of the ommatidial angle. In human vision, it is found that a long single opaque line subtending a visual angle of only 0.5 second of arc can be detected against an evenly-and brightly-lit background (4). This thickness would correspond to that of *one* of the black bars of Fig. 66, seen through

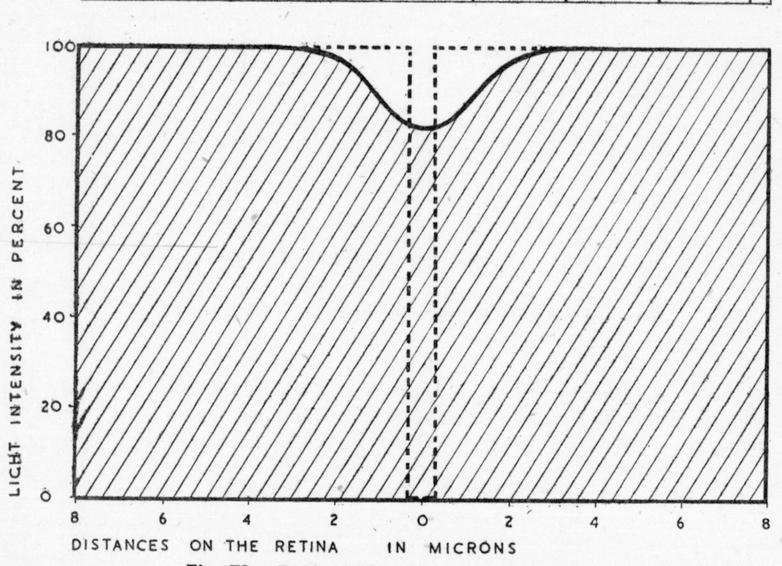

Fig. 72. Retinal image of a thin wire.

Light intensity distribution (full line) in the retinal image of a thin black wire, whose geometrial image is shown by the dotted line, and corresponds to a visual angle of 6.8 seconds. The light distribution corresponding to the smallest resolvable angle, 0.5 second, is of similar shape, but so flat and so near the 100 per cent. line that it can hardly be shown in a drawing of this size. The scale on the top of the figure corresponds to a row of retinal cones 2.3 microns in diameter.

(After Hecht and Mintz (4), *J. Gen. Physiol.*, **22**, 593, 1939.)

a perfectly-transparent atmosphere, from a distance of about 3 kilometres. The image of such a thin line on the retina is very different from its geometrical projection on it, as shown in Fig. 72. In the case of the highest resolution mentioned above, the geometrical width is only about one-sixtieth of the diameter of a single cone. Due to diffraction effects, the image becomes a blurred shadow, the width of which is many times the width of the geometrical image. The row of foveal cones occupying the centre of this long shadow suffers a decrease of light-intensity of about one per cent. in comparison with the intensity received by the other cones. It is probable that still finer black lines cannot be seen because the decrease of intensity produced by their image is too low to be detected by the cones (4).

It may be noted here that there is, of course, no problem corresponding to the above for an illuminated slit on a dark background; for, in this case, the slit—however thin—always becomes visible when it is sufficiently brightly illuminated.

LIMITATIONS SET BY THE WAVE-LENGTH OF LIGHT IN OPTICAL INSTRUMENTS

The explanation of the maximum resolving power of the human eye is very complicated, and as yet incompletely solved, because of the number of different factors which come into play; some of which are special to particular test-objects used in measuring acuity. It will be noted that the resolving power of the human eye is so good that the diffraction effects due to the wave properties of light are very strongly felt. These are the same effects which limit the resolving power of all optical instruments, such as the microscope.

The magnification given by a microscope can be increased indefinitely, but its resolving power cannot. That is to say, a larger image can be obtained, but at one point the details of the image fail to become sharper. This occurs for details having dimensions near the wave-length of light. It is interesting to note that this, in particular, is the case for the dimensions of retinal structures: a cone or a rod, for instance, has a diameter equal to only a few wave-lengths of visible light. Fine details inside a rod cannot, therefore, be distinguished with certainty; not because of the imperfection of the microscope, but because of the limit set by the wave-properties of light itself. This must be borne in mind when examining microscopical anatomical drawings, such as some of those reproduced in this book (5).

BIBLIOGRAPHY AND NOTES

(1) HECHT, S. (1931). *Bulletin No.* 4 *of the Howe Laboratory of Ophthalmology*, Harvard Medical School, Cambridge, Mass.

(2) SHLAER, S., SMITH, E. L., and CHASE, A. M. (1942). " Visual acuity and illumination in different spectral regions," *J. Gen. Physiol.*, **25**, 553–569.

(3) SHLAER, S. (1937). " The Relation between visual acuity and illumination," *J. Gen. Physiol.*, **21**, 165–188.

(4) HECHT, S., and MINTZ, E. U. (1939). " The visibility of single lines at various illuminations and the retinal basis of visual resolution," *J. Gen. Physiol.*, **22**, 593–612.

The idea that the maximum resolving power of the eye is determined by its ability to detect differences of light intensity was put forward by HARTRIDGE (1922), *J. Physiol.*, **57**, 52.

(5) It is well known that radiations of much shorter wave-length than visible light, namely, X-rays and electron rays, are used to investigate the finer structure of matter. See e.g. BRAGG, W. L. (1933). *The Crystalline State*, London; PIRENNE, M. H. (1946). *The Diffraction of X-rays and Electrons by Free Molecules*, Cambridge; ZWORIKIN, V. K., MORTON, G. A., RAMBER, G. E. G., HILLIER, J., and VANCE, A. W. (1945). *Electron Optics and the Electron Microscope*, New York.

Chapter XI

VARIATION OF ACUITY WITH LIGHT INTENSITY

NATURE OF THE VARIATION

THE fact that we can, as a rule, see finer details when the light is brighter, is so familiar that we may never have stopped to consider it. Yet the reasons for this increase of precision on the part of the visual system are not fully established. It is not due to the fact that the pupil of the human eye, by contracting in bright light, increases the accuracy of the optical system, for experiments such as those of Fig. 70, are made using an artificial pupil. While the size of the pupil thus remains constant at high and low intensities, the decrease of acuity with decreasing intensity is in no way prevented. Moreover, the variation of visual acuity with intensity occurs in similar ways in eyes as different as those of insects and man. It must therefore be expected to be due to a property of the retina or of the nervous system.

As the intensity increases, a subject whose acuity is being measured uses more and more central parts of his retina. It can be presumed that peripheral areas are more sensitive to light and less accurate as far as acuity is concerned, while central areas are less sensitive to light but more accurate. In one and the same region of the retina, however, visual acuity varies within very wide limits as the intensity changes. This is the fact which mostly demands explanation.

At a low intensity, the acuity is only a fraction of the maximum value attained at high intensities; it is as if the retina had been exchanged for another retina made of a coarser mosaic of light-detectors. But there is no such obvious anatomical change in the distribution or nervous connections of rods and cones in the human eye, or in the arrangement of ommatidia in the insect eye. A theory has been put forward to reconcile these two facts, according to which acuity increases with increasing retinal illumination because the various individual detectors of light in the retina have different sensitivities, so that more detectors are active at higher than at lower illuminations (1). In one and the same region of the retina, the mosaic of detectors would thus become *functionally* finer at higher brightnesses, maximum acuity being reached when all the detectors are active.

Complications are, in general, introduced in such a theory because of the fact that, when a detector is excited, the magnitude and other characteristics of the discharge of impulses in the corresponding nerve-fibre vary with the intensity of the light-stimulus. Moveover, the hypothesis that the various detectors of light in one and the same region of the retina have individual differences of sensitivity large enough to explain the facts, appears rather of an *ad hoc* nature. These difficulties, however, need not make one abandon the main idea that the retinal mosaic becomes functionally finer at higher illuminations.

QUANTUM FLUCTUATIONS AND THE VARIATION OF VISUAL ACUITY WITH INTENSITY

There is evidence that the above idea applies to the variation of acuity in the periphery of the human eye at very low intensities, near the absolute threshold(2). Here, the hypothesis that the detectors have various sensitivities is unnecessary, because of quantum fluctuations occurring in the absorption of light by the retina.

As has been seen in Chapter VIII, when a retinal detector is exposed to light, there is only a certain probability p of its being excited, p going progressively from zero to unity as the intensity is increased. The detector, so far left undefined, is here the group of rods connected to one nerve-fibre, acting as a unit, and having a certain " receptive field " on the retina. Under certain conditions, as has been seen, the variation of p with intensity can be quantitatively explained by the purely physical fluctuations which occur in the small number of light quanta absorbed by the detector. Imagine, then, that a retinal area containing a number N of independent and identical detectors is illuminated for a short time. The probability of exciting one of the detectors being p, the mean number of detectors excited is pN, and this number tends to N as p tends to unity. If the number N of detectors is, say, 1,000, and the probability p, 1 per cent., the average number pN of detectors excited will be only 10. If p is 10 per cent., the number pN will be 100; if p is 50 per cent., pN will be 500; and if p = 100 per cent., pN, of course, is equal to 1,000. The retinal mosaic, therefore, would become finer as the light-intensity increases, although its anatomy remains perfectly unchanged, and all the detectors are assumed to be quite identical in all properties, including light-sensitivity (cf. Fig. 73).

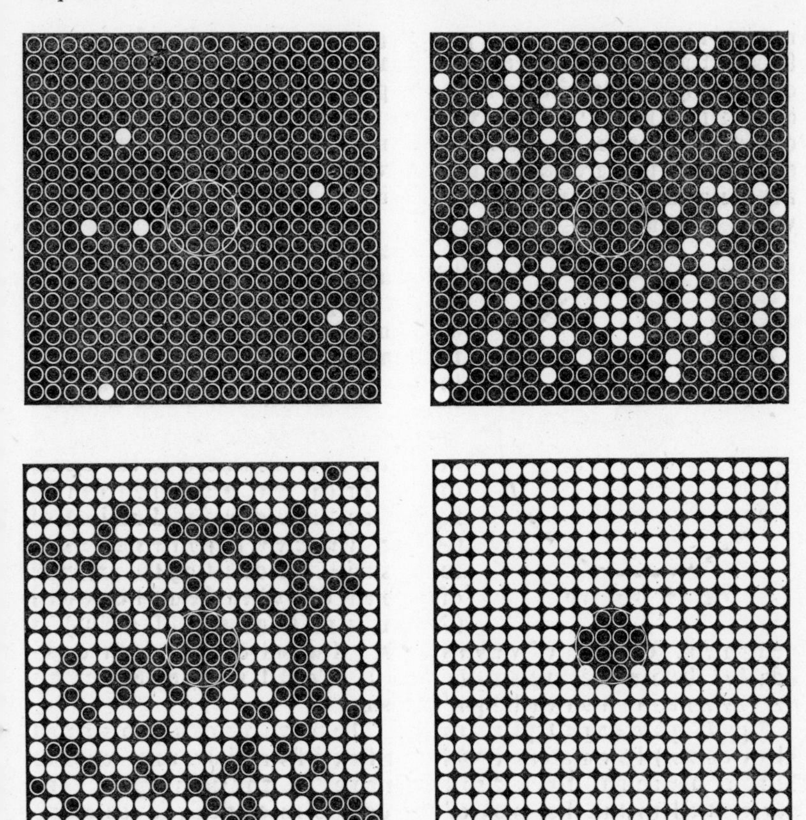

Fig. 73. Schematic representation of a retinal mosaic becoming functionally finer as the illumination increases.

The small circles represent light detectors : the white ones are excited detectors ; the empty ones are inactive. The large circle in the centre is the image of a black disc. See text.

If one restricts one's attention to these low intensities, at which the absolute threshold of only part of the total number of detectors is reached, the complications arising from the variations of frequency in the discharge of impulses by the nerve fibre do not arise. For, if the retinal image of a dark object placed against a uniformly lit background falls in between excited detectors, that is, on detectors which are not discharging impulses in any case, the presence or absence of this image does not make any difference to the pattern of stimulation, and the object thus cannot be seen. In such a case the extent to which the excited detectors are responding is irrelevant: what matters is whether the dark image prevents the stimulation of detectors which otherwise would be stimulated, or not.

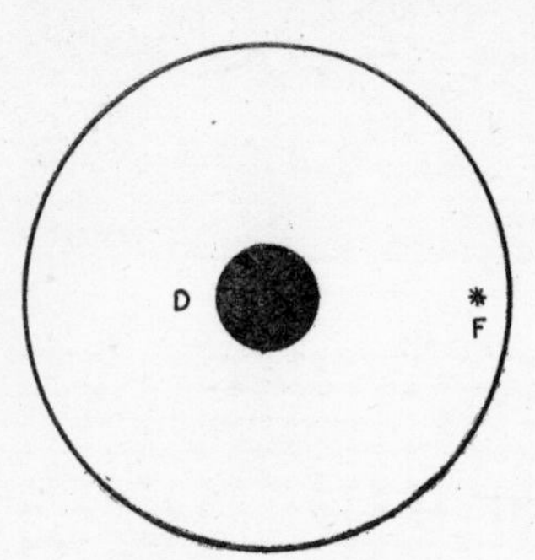

Fig. 74. See text.

Experiments were made in the following way to test this theory: a subject using his right eye, fixes through a 2 mm. artificial pupil, a luminous fixation point F, placed 20° temporarily to the centre of a circular opal glass screen, the diameter of which subtends an angle of 46° at the eye (Fig. 74). A black disc D is suspended in the centre of the screen, and white light can be flashed on the screen for durations of 0·03 sec. The screen brightness necessary to the subject for detecting the presence of the black disc when the light is flashed (50 per cent. frequency of seeing) is determined for discs of various sizes. The subject has been dark-adapted before the experiment and is allowed time to recover his dark adaptation after each light exposure.

Fig. 75 gives some typical results. The measurements (crosses and black circles) lie on a curve which at first falls rapidly, then tends to become horizontal, for a disc of diameter 2°, and falls again. The curve fitted to the first part of the data is theoretical; it represents the size of the area inside which, at different brightnesses, one detector must on the average be expected to be excited, under the assumption that each detector needs to absorb $n = 5$ quanta or more in order to be excited. The plot being a double logarithmic one, only the shapes of the curves, that is, relative values, matter in fitting them to one another. Now for the same subject the experimental curves giving the probability of seeing a circular luminous field 10 minutes in diameter placed 20° peripherally, at various brightnesses, have a shape corresponding to $n = 5$ or 6. The agreement between observation and theory thus seems satisfactory, especially if it is considered

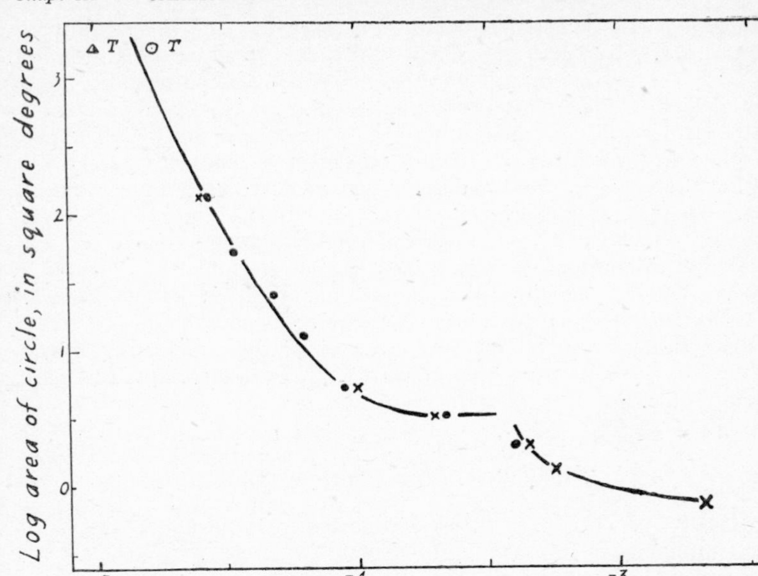

Fig. 75. Variation of acuity at very low intensities.

See text. The abscissae of the two points marked *T* on the figure give determinations of the absolute threshold of visibility of the large screen itself when it is empty ; their ordinate corresponds to the screen area.

that the latter is a first approximation which does not take into account the overlapping of detectors over detectors, and of retinal image over detectors, nor the possibility that all detectors are not identical. These limitations are likely to affect the shape of the curve, especially in the vicinity of the plateau. If biological, as well as physical, fluctuations affect the behaviour of the detectors, the reasoning still remains essentially valid, provided these variations are also random in nature. At brightnesses higher than those of the plateau, the ordinates fall again and the acuity increases. It seems that this must be due to another mechanism coming into play.

According to the above interpretation, the ordinate at which the curve becomes horizontal should give a rough value of the area covered by one detector—perhaps too large a value on account of overlapping. The detector area would therefore have a diameter of about 2°, corresponding to 0·58 mm. on the retina, and would contain about 40,000 rods. This approximate value of the detector area is of the same order as those obtained in man and other vertebrates by other methods (2, 3) (cf. section on receptive fields in Chapter V).

It is interesting to see that the visual angle corresponding to this area, being 2°, is equal to twice the ommatidial angle of the bee. If acuity is defined as the reciprocal of the angular diameter of the black disc in minutes of arc, it has here a value of $1/(2 \times 60) = 0{\cdot}008$. This is half the value of the maximum acuity of the bee. It is therefore possible for a man to acquire an idea of the accuracy of the vision of insects by using his eyes at light intensities which are only, say, twenty times the intensity at which a large area becomes at all visible.

BIBLIOGRAPHY AND NOTES

(1) HECHT, S. (1928). "The relation between visual acuity and illumination," *J. Gen. Physiology*, **11**, 255–281.

(2) PIRENNE, M. H. (1945). "On the variation of visual acuity with light intensity," *Proc. Cambridge Phil. Soc.*, **42**, 78–82.

(3) Another theory gives a different explanation of the variation of acuity with light intensity. It supposes that the retinal mosaic is functionally coarser at lower intensities because the nervous connexions in the retina or in the brain change at low intensities. This would occur in such a way, for instance, that a group of ommatidia in an insect eye would become connected with the same fibre, thus forming a larger unit in a new and coarser mosaic. This larger unit would summate the effects of light on its constituent ommatidia and thus be more sensitive to light (BUDDENBROCK, W. v. (1937). *Grundriss der vergleichenden Physiologie*, 2d. ed., 2 vol., Berlin). There seems to be little direct evidence in favour of this hypothesis. If it were true the area of each of the new functional units should be of the same order of magnitude as the details which can just be detected by the eye at the corresponding brightness. In the case of the dark-adapted human eye, the area in which true summation of the effect of light occurs is of the order of 1° in

diameter. (In the case of patches of light separated by more than this angular diameter the lowering of intensity threshold which is observed when the number of patches is increased, can be explained simply by the consequent increase in the probability of seeing at least one of the patches. This corresponds to what occurs when the sensitivity of the two eyes is compared to the sensitivity of one eye, as explained further in Chapter XVI on the Eyes and the Brain. See STILES, W. S. (1944). *Proc. Phys. Soc.*, **56**, 329, and ref. (2) above.) Fig. 75, however, shows that at the lowest brightnesses the smallest " detail " visible is a disc which may be ten times larger in diameter and one hundred times larger in area than the area in which summation occurs. This discrepancy would seem to make the alternative theory just explained untenable in the case of human vision in the conditions of the experiment described by Fig. 75. Experimental work on this problem is still in progress.

Chapter XII

NEWTON'S DOCTRINE OF COLOUR

SIR ISAAC NEWTON'S *Opticks* (1), the first edition of which was published in 1704, forms the basis of modern scientific theories of colour. According to Newton, physical light exists in an infinite number of different varieties, incapable of being changed into one another by reflexion or refraction. Each of them is characterized by a definite degree of refrangibility, that is, by the property that a ray of this light is bent to a definite extent when passing through a glass prism. These different kinds of light, which Newton called " homogeneal " lights, are, of course, the various monochromatic lights of to-day's physics, which are now characterized by their wave-length rather than by their refrangibility.

Thus all the colours of the objects we see are caused by the action on our eyes of such " homogeneal ", monochromatic, lights occurring either pure or mixed in various proportions.

It is clear that Newton's doctrine is as important for the physiology of vision as for physics. It was at the time a very new and bold conception, which met with considerable opposition. The poet Goethe (2) wrote books attacking it, and apparently believed that his " refutation " of Newton would become one of his main titles to fame. It must be recognized that the elaboration in the physiology of vision of Newton's doctrine, which has become current physical knowledge, is yet far from complete and has sometimes been obscured by misunderstandings.

THE VISIBLE SPECTRUM

Newton describes as follows the fundamental experiment he made to prove that " The Light of the Sun consists of Rays differently refrangible ".

" *Exper*. 3. In a very dark chamber, at a round Hole, about one third Part of an Inch broad, made in the Shut of a Window, I placed a Glass Prism, whereby the Beam of the Sun's Light, which came in at that Hole, might be refracted upwards toward the opposite Wall of the Chamber, and there form a colour'd Image of the Sun." (Fig. 76.)

"This Image or Spectrum PT was coloured, being red at its least refracted end T, and violet at its most refracted end P, and yellow green and blue in the intermediate Spaces. Which agrees with the first Proposition, that Lights which differ in Colour, do also differ in Refrangibility."

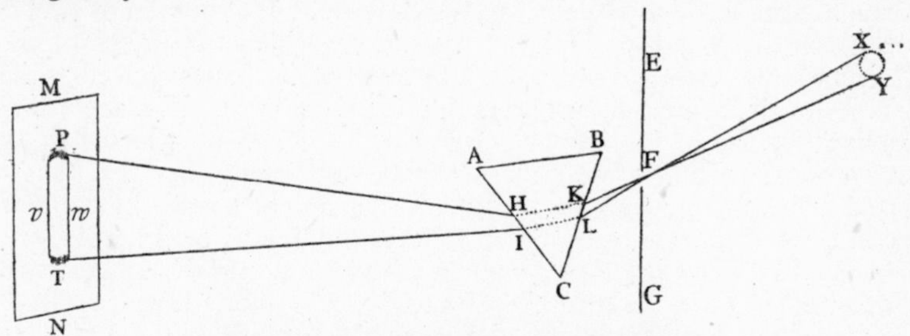

Fig. 76. "Experiment 3" of Newton.
See text.
(From Sir Isaac Newton's *Opticks* (1), London, 1704. Reproduced by permission of the Cambridge University Library.)

This experiment, however, does not give a very good separation of the various monochromatic lights of which sunlight is composed. For the spectrum is formed of a series of innumerable monochromatic images of the sun, all of which are rather large circles—the dark room with the opening F acting as a pinhole camera—and the various monochromatic images largely overlap in the spectrum PT (Fig. 77). Newton

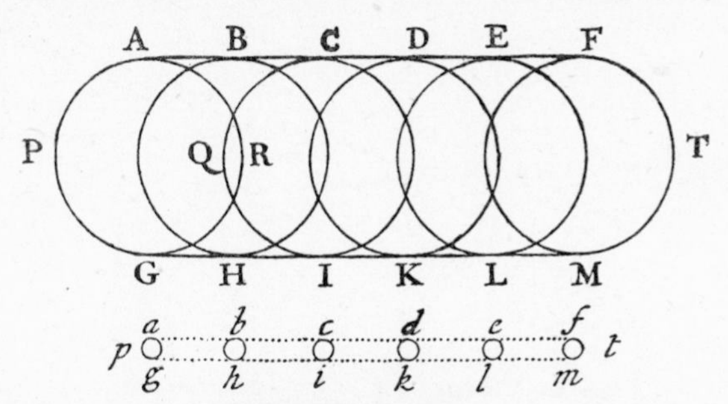

Fig. 77. See text.
(From Sir Isaac Newton's *Opticks* (1), London, 1704. Reproduced by permission of the Cambridge University Library.)

found a way of reducing the size of the various monochromatic patches of light without changing the length of the spectrum, thereby forming a narrow spectrum *pt* of much greater purity. His device contains the essential features of a modern spectroscope.

" *Exper.* 11. In the Sun's Light let into my darken'd Chamber through a small round Hole in my Window-shut, at about ten or twelve Feet from the Window, I placed a Lens, by which the Image of the Hole might be distinctly cast upon a Sheet of white Paper, placed at the distance of six, eight, ten, or twelve Feet from the Lens. For, according to the difference of the Lenses I used various distances, which I think not worth the while to describe. Then immediately after the Lens I placed a Prism, by which the trajected Light might be refracted either upwards or side-ways, and thereby the round Image, which the Lens alone did cast upon the Paper might be drawn out into a long one with Parallel Sides, as in the third Experiment. This oblong Image I let fall upon another Paper at about the same distance from the Prism as before, moving the Paper either towards the Prism or from it, until I found the just distance where the Rectilinear Sides of the Image became most distinct."

"In the twenty-fourth Figure [Fig. 78], F represents the Circular Hole in the Window-shut, MN the Lens, whereby the Image or Species of that Hole is cast distinctly upon a Paper at I, ABC the Prism, whereby

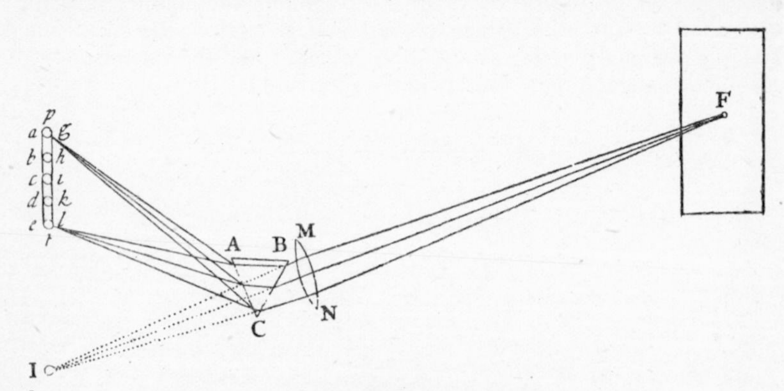

Fig. 78. " Experiment 11 " of Newton.

See text.

(From Sir Isaac Newton's *Opticks* (I), London, 1704. Reproduced by permission of the Cambridge University Library.)

the Rays are at their emerging out of the Lens refracted from I towards another Paper at pt, and the round Image at I is turned into an oblong Image pt falling on that other Paper. This image pt consists of Circles placed one after another in a Rectilinear Order; and these Cirlces are equal to the Circle I, and consequently answer in magnitude to the Hole F; and therefore by diminishing that Hole they may be at pleasure diminished, whilst their Centers remain in their Places. By this means I made the Breadth of the Image pt to be forty times, and sometimes sixty or seventy times less than its Length" [Fig. 77].

Newton also used a slit instead of a hole in his spectroscope:

"Yet instead of the Circular Hole F, 'tis better to substitute an oblong Hole shaped like a long Parallelogram with its Length parallel to the Prism ABC. For if this Hole be an Inch or two long, and but a tenth or twentieth Part of an Inch broad, or narrower; the Light of the Image pt will be as simple as before, or simpler, and the Image will become much broader, and therefore more fit to have Experiments try'd in its Light than before."

"*THE PERMANENT COLOURS OF NATURAL BODIES*"

On the basis of these experiments, Newton explained such colour phenomena as the rainbow, in which sunlight is decomposed into a spectrum when passing through a rain drop, and he particularly studied the "permanent colours" of natural objects. Having obtained, as we have seen, a solar spectrum of high purity which appeared, from p to t (Fig. 77), "tinged with this Series of Colours, violet, indigo, blue, green, yellow, orange, red, together with all their intermediate Degrees in a continual Succession perpetually varying" he illuminated various coloured objects with pure spectral lights. He found that "all white, grey, red, yellow, green, blue, violet Bodies, as Paper, Ashes, red Lead, Orpiment, Indico Bise, Gold, Silver, Copper, Grass, blue Flowers, Violets, Bubbles of Water tinged with various Colours, Peacock's Feathers, the Tincture of *Lignum Nephriticum*, and such-like, in red homogeneal Light appeared totally red, in blue Light totally blue, in green Light totally green, and so of other Colours. In the homogeneal Light of any Colour they all appeared totally of that same Colour, with this only Difference, that some of them reflected that Light more strongly, others more faintly."

He later says: "if Cinnaber and *ultra*-marine blue, or some other full blue be held together in the red homogeneal Light, they will both appear red, but the Cinnaber will appear of a strongly luminous and resplendent red, and the *ultra*-marine blue of a faint obscure and dark red; and if they be held together in the blue homogeneal Light, they will both appear blue, but the *ultra*-marine will appear of a strongly luminous and resplendent blue, and the Cinnaber of a faint and dark blue."

The conclusion is that the permanent colours of natural objects " arise from hence, that some natural Bodies reflect some sorts of Rays, others other sorts more copiously than the rest " . . . " For if Bodies by Reflexion cannot in the least change the Colour of any one sort of Rays, they cannot appear colour'd by any other means than by reflecting those which either are of their own Colour, or which by mixture must produce it."

It follows that if the reflecting power of the surface of any object, such as a white or coloured sheet of paper, is known for each wave-length of the spectrum, this information defines completely the colour characteristics of this surface. That is, it defines exactly the physical composition of the light reflected by the surface under any known conditions of illumination.

Modern technique has made it possible to measure exactly such *spectral reflexion curves* (3). The method used is essentially as follows. The surface under consideration is illuminated with light of a given wave-length, obtained using a spectroscope, and the physical intensity of the reflected light is measured and compared with the intensity of the incident beam. Their ratio gives the reflecting power for this wave-length. The procedure is repeated for each wave-length in turn. Plate IV gives spectral reflextion curves obtained in this way for paper coated with different pigments. The characteristic spectral reflexion curve of the surface of an object is a property depending, in a complicated way, upon the chemical nature of the substances forming the object and upon their physical state and arrangement in the object.

Let us consider an object illuminated by any given source of light. The *spectral energy distribution* (3) of the light of this source can be determined; that is, the energy emitted by the source for each wave-length of the spectrum can be measured. This is done using again a spectroscope in order to produce a spectrum of the light of the source—as was done by Newton for the sun—and placing a suitable instrument for measuring the energy of the light in each part of the spectrum in turn. Now multiplying the energy emitted by the source at each wave-length by the reflecting power of the surface of the object for the same wave-length, the spectral energy distribution of the light reflected by the surface is obtained. The amount of light of each wave-length which the surface sends to the eye when it is illuminated by this particular source is thus known. In particular, if a monochromatic source is used, as in the above experiments made by Newton on cinnaber and ultra-marine, the calculation gives simply the intensity of the monochromatic light reflected by the object. The spectral distribution of the light reflected by the object could of course be determined directly, with the same result, as it was done for the light of the source itself, but in practice it is often more convenient to operate as explained above.

It is clear from this that all that is permanent in connexion with the colour of natural objects is their spectral reflexion curve. This is a physical property, which the eye alone cannot determine. The physical light reflected by the objects into the eye is anything but permanent in composition, since it varies with the source of illumination.

EFFECT OF LIGHT INTENSITY

In this chapter so far we have considered mostly the *relative* amounts of radiation of various wave-lengths emitted by light sources or reflected by objects. The *absolute* intensities of the radiations have also a great importance in connection with colour. For instance, as has been seen earlier in this book, all objects appear colourless at low intensities when the rods of the retina are alone functioning. In bright daylight, many objects look grey, or brown. Grey objects send to our eye light similar to that sent by white objects, but in smaller quantity, as shown already by Newton. He took a dark grey mixture of pigments in powder form:

" I rubbed it thickly upon the Floor of my Chamber, where the Sun shone upon it through the opened Casement; and by it, in the shadow, I laid a Piece of white Paper of the same Bigness. Then going from them to the distance of 12 or 18 Feet, so that I could not discern the Unevenness of the Surface of the Powder, nor the little Shadows let fall from the gritty Particles thereof; the Powder appeared intensely white, so as to transcend even the Paper itself in Whiteness, especially if the Paper were a little shaded from the Light of the Clouds, and then the Paper compared with the Powder appeared of such a grey Colour as the Powder had done before. But by laying the Paper where the Sun shines through the Glass of the Window, or by shutting the Window that the Sun might shine through the Glass upon the Powder, and by such other fit Means of increasing or decreasing the Lights wherewith the Powder and

Paper were illuminated, the Light wherewith the Powder is illuminated may be made stronger in such a due Proportion than the Light wherewith the Paper is illuminated, that they shall both appear exactly alike in Whiteness. For when I was trying this, a Friend coming to visit me, I stopp'd him at the Door, and before I told him what the Colours were, or what I was doing; I asked him, Which of the two Whites were the best, and wherein they differed? And after he had at that distance viewed them well, he answer'd, that they were both good Whites, and that he could not say which was best, nor wherein their Colours differed."

Similar experiments show that a dark brown paper really reflects light which appears bright red or yellow when its intensity is sufficiently increased.

Thus "*all the colours of the universe which are made by light and depend not on the power of imagination*" *are caused by monochromatic lights, or by mixture of monochromatic lights, falling into our eyes.* The absolute, as well as the relative, intensity of the lights determine the resulting appearance of the coloured object, when due account is taken of the light sent by neighbouring objects, and of the physiological state of the organism, such as the state of dark or light adaptation of the eye.

BIBLIOGRAPHY

(1) NEWTON, SIR ISAAC. *Opticks, or a Treatise of the Reflections, Refractions, Inflections and Colours of Light*, London, 1st. ed., 1704; 4th ed., 1730.

The 4th ed., the last corrected by Newton, is available in a modern reprint, London, 1931.

The quotations in the above chapter are all taken from Newton's *Opticks*.

(2) GOETHE, V. (1810). *Zur Farbenlehre*, 2 vol., Tübingen.

(3) HARDY, A. C. and PERRIN, F. H. (1932). *The Principles of Optics*, New York and London.

Chapter XIII

NORMAL COLOUR VISION

DIFFERENT PHYSICAL LIGHTS MAY APPEAR THE SAME TO THE EYE

THE analysis of light by such instruments as the spectroscope reveals that there are lights which appear identical to the normal human eye and which nevertheless have very different physical compositions. For instance a mixture of monochromatic yellow light and monochromatic blue light can be made which appears identical to the light of the sun. The effect produced on the observer by the mixture of these two so-called complementary lights is thus the same as the effect of the mixture of all the monochromatic lights of the spectrum, of which sunlight is formed.

A practised musician can distinguish in the sound of an orchestra the sound of the individual instruments; a trained observer may even hear the various pure tones and overtones which compose the sound of a musical instrument. The situation is entirely different with the eye. No one is able to decide from what he sees whether, for instance, a certain white light is sun-light, or a mixture of only two monochromatic lights. No one is able to say with certainty what are the components of a mixture of lights which strikes his retina (1). It might be objected that a painter apparently knows of what " colours " a given tint is composed, but this only means that the painter knows what pigments he must mix on his palette in order to obtain this tint. His is an empirical knowledge of the laws of the mixing of pigments, which are quite different from the laws of the mixing of lights. (Cf. Plate IV.)

Using a photometric field of the kind mentioned in connexion with the Purkinje phenomenon, it is possible to make a systematic study of all such " confusions " made by the eye between lights which are physically different. The light to be investigated is made to fill one half A of the field, while various other lights or mixtures of lights are made to fill the other half B (Fig. 79). It is thus possible to determine whether there is another physical light which, filling B, can be made to appear identical with the light filling A when its intensity is suitably adjusted.

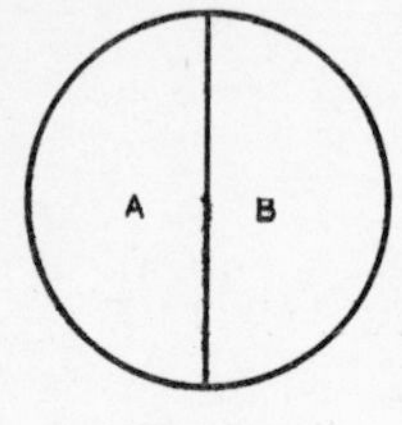

Fig. 79.

The results to be described presently refer to the use of a small field AB having a diameter subtending only 1° or 2° at the eye. The field is looked at directly. The intensities used are fairly high, well above the range in which the Purkinje phenomenon takes place (2). These experimental conditions make it very probable that the results obtained refer exclusively to the cones of the fovea.

LAW OF ADDITIVITY OF COLOUR MATCHES

A first fundamental law derived from such studies is the following: *If two physical lights which appear identical are mixed one by one with two other lights which also appear identical to the eye, the two new resulting mixtures will appear identical* (3).

For instance, let us take two lights X and Y, mixed or monochromatic, which appear identical to the eye, having, say, a green colour. Let us take another pair of lights U and V which also appear of the same brightness and colour, having, say, a red colour. Let us now add X to U and Y to V. We obtain two new lights, which may appear neither red nor green, but yellow. These two lights will appear identical to the eye. Identical-looking lights added to identical-looking lights thus give identical-looking lights.

Since increasing the intensity of a light is of course the same thing as adding more of the same light to its original amount, it follows immediately from this law, as a particular case, that colour matches are independent of the intensity level at which they are made. If the two lights filling the fields A and B appear identical to the eye, and if the physical intensity of each light is, say, doubled, the two fields A and B, now brighter than before, will still appear identical to one another. It is clear that this law introduces great regularity in the facts of colour mixture. It is a familiar phenomenon, at least in its implications, but it nevertheless constitutes a remarkable physiological property of the eye. The existence of the Purkinje phenomenon, which causes the breakdown of this law of additivity at lower brightnesses and in larger retinal fields, shows that, *a priori*, this property of the eye was by no means necessarily to be expected to exist at higher brightnesses and for central vision.

A SYSTEM OF CLASSIFICATION OF LIGHTS

Another general conclusion derived from matching experiments is the following:

Any existing light can be matched

(a) *either against white light*
(b) *or against a monochromatic light,*
(c) *or against a purple light*, that is, a light made of a mixture of extreme spectral red and extreme spectral blue light
(d) *or against a mixture of white light plus a monochromatic light, or plus a purple light* (3).

This experimental law can be used as the basis of a general classification of lights from the point of view of their colour. Outside the laboratory (d) is the case most frequently met. Suppose, for instance, that a grass lawn is illuminated by the sun. The light reflected by the grass can be matched with white light plus a certain quantity of a specified monochromatic light, which in this case will as a rule belong to the green or yellow-green region of the spectrum. The colour of the grass under those conditions is then exactly defined as far as normal human colour vision is concerned, if the intensity as well as the composition of the matching light is known. It must be noted that in such a case we are dealing with the actual light reflected by the grass under the particular conditions of the moment. As has been seen in the preceding chapter, while the spectral reflexion curve of the grass is a permanent characteristic of it, the light actually reflected depends also upon the source of illumination. This reflected light will be different when the grass is illuminated by another source than the sun, for instance by the blue sky or, at night, by an electric bulb or a neon lamp. In each case, however, the light reflected can again be specified by the mixture of white light plus a monochromatic or a purple light which matches it. If the grass is illuminated by a single monochromatic light, as in Newton's experiment quoted above, then its colour is of course defined by the wave-length of this monochromatic light—which, needless to say, can belong to any part, say, the red or the blue, as well as to the green part of the spectrum. It will be noted that such a classification of lights would have little practical utility without the constancy which is due to the law of additivity of colour matches. For if this law did not apply, the colour specification of a compound light would as a rule change for each different intensity of this light.

THE SPECTRAL LIGHTS

The visible spectrum can be divided into four regions (3, 4) (Fig. 80). In the red end region, extending from the extreme red end to 655mμ, all wave-lengths can be matched with light of wave-length $\lambda = 655$mμ. The only difference which can be observed in this region between monochromatic lights of different wave-lengths is one of brightness.

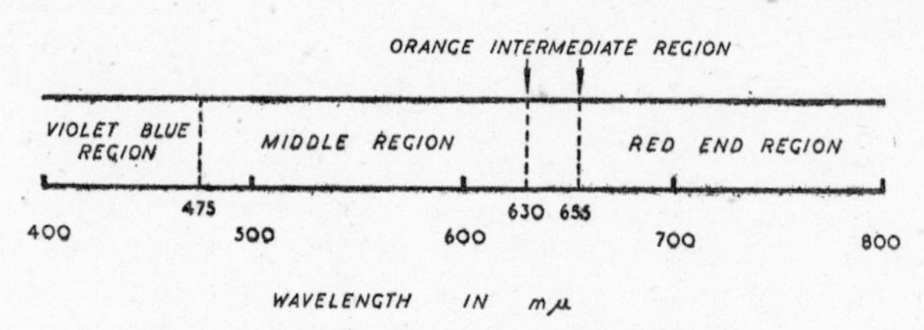

Fig. 80. Regions of the visible spectrum.

In the orange intermediate region, extending from 630 to 655mμ, all lights can be matched by suitable mixtures of lights of the two wave-lengths which limit this region, i.e. 630 and 655mμ. At the other end of the spectrum (4), in the blue-violet region, extending for the violet end, 400mμ, to 475mμ, light of all wave-lengths can be matched by suitable mixtures of light of $\lambda = 475$mμ with light of $\lambda = 400$mμ.

In the middle region, extending from 475 to 630mμ, the situation, however, is quite different. It is not possible here to match exactly a wave-length by a mixture of two others. Neither is it possible to match it by a mixture of three, or more, wave-lengths (5).

It is often possible, however, to match exactly with a mixture of two monochromatic lights a third monochromatic light, *provided this third light is mixed with a suitable amount of white light.* It will be observed that this is in agreement with the law mentioned in the preceding section. Thus it is possible to find, for instance, a mixture of 460mμ and 530mμ which matches exactly a mixture of 500mμ and white light:

Half field A		*Half field B*
light of $\lambda = 500$mμ mixed in suitable proportion with white light	appears completely identical to	light of $\lambda = 460$mμ mixed in suitable proportion with light of $\lambda = 530$mμ

Similar matches can be made when, in the half field A, the light of 500mμ is replaced by light of any wave-length between 460 and 530mμ. In the same way, it is possible to obtain a match between binary mixtures, e.g. of 530 and 650mμ and mixtures of white light with monochromatic lights of any wave-length between 530 and 650mμ.

Contrary to what appears to be sometimes believed, it is *not* possible to place on one side of the photometric field certain mixtures of three given monochromatic lights which would match exactly all the monochromatic lights of the spectrum placed on the other side of the field in turn.

TRICHROMATIC COEFFICIENT CURVES

Notwithstanding what has just been said above, *there are very important matches, which can be made using three monochromatic lights, the same throughout the experiment, and each spectral light in turn.* These matches are of a special kind, in that the three " primary " monochromatic lights are not placed together in the same half of the photometric field (3, 6, 7).

Let us for instance take as primaries, lights of wave-lengths 460, 530 and 650mμ. Let us consider a fourth light of, say, $\lambda = 500$mμ. If we mix this fourth light with light of 650mμ, the resulting light can be matched by a suitable mixture of 460 and 530mμ.

A		B
light of $\lambda = 500$mμ mixed in suitable proportion with light of $\lambda = 650$mμ	appears identical to	light of $\lambda = 460$mμ mixed in suitable proportion with light of $\lambda = 530$mμ

Similar matches can be made for light of any wave-length λ instead of 500mμ; but there are the following differences, according to the region of the spectrum to which the wave-length λ belongs. In the above example, light of 650mμ had to be added to λ in order to match a mixture of the other two primaries, 460 and 530mμ. For λ in other regions of the spectrum, 460mμ has sometimes to be added to λ in order to match a mixture of 530 and 650mμ; and sometimes it is the 530mμ primary which has to be added to the wave-length λ in order to match a mixture of the two other remaining primaries.

The results of such experiments are expressed quantitatively in Fig. 81. The abscissa gives the wave-length λ investigated. The ordinates give the relative amounts, in special units, of the primary lights of wave-lengths 460, 530 and 650mμ. By a special convention the amount of primary light which has to be added to the wave-length λ investigated is represented by a negative ordinate. Thus for a wave-length λ = 500mμ, the ordinates are about $-$ 0·23 for the 650mμ primary, + 0·46 for the 460mμ primary, and + 0·77 for the 530mμ primary. This means that mixing 0·46 unit of light of 460mμ with 0·77 unit of light of 530mμ on one half of the photometric field, and mixing on the other half of the field 0·23 units of 650mμ with a sufficient amount of 500mμ, the two halves will appear identical. It will be noted that the negative values of the ordinates are introduced purely as a convention. Quantities of light entering the eye, unless they are zero, are, needless to say, always positive. All quantities of light used in the experiments could be plotted as positive ordinate by using two graphs, one for each half of the photometric field, instead of one single graph as in Fig. 81.

The data represented by Fig. 81 refer, of course, to the particular set of primaries which has been chosen. Similar curves can be obtained for *any* other set of primaries, provided these primaries be lights which cannot be matched one with another. The data referring to any set of primaries can be shown to be quantitatively related to those obtained using any other set (8). This is a consequence of the law of additivity of colour mixture.

It follows that there is nothing fundamental in the " primaries ": one is dealing, in each match, with 4 wave-lengths, among which none occupies a privileged position. It may then be best to express the fundamental facts of observation relating to the trichromatic coefficient curves as follows:—

Given any 4 spectral lights, it is always possible to place 2 of them—suitably chosen—in one half of the field, 2 in the other, and, by adjusting the intensities of 3 of them, to make the two halves of the field appear indistinguishable to the eye.

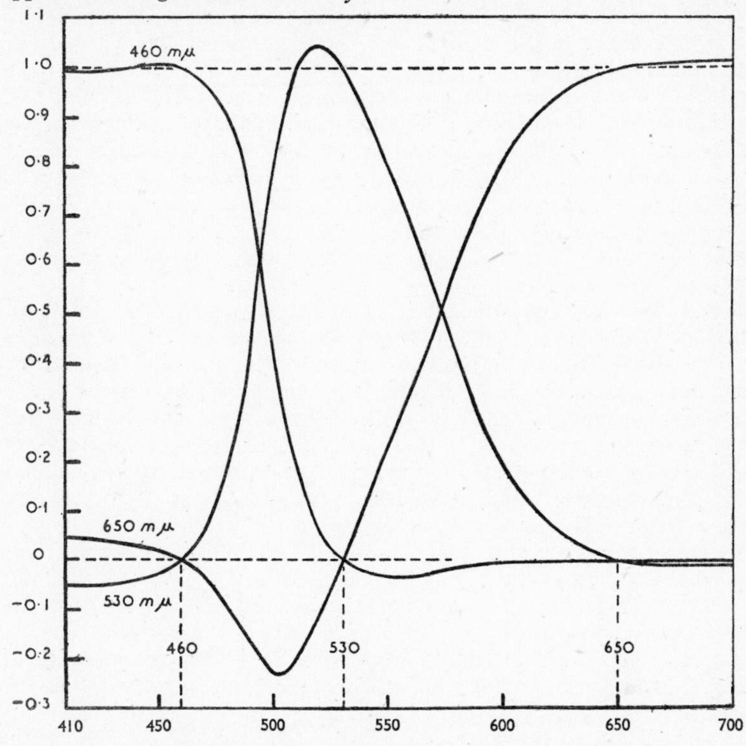

Fig. 81. Trichromatic coefficient curves.
Explanation in text. Plotted from the numerical data of Wright (7).

Data such as those given in Fig. 81 are of fundamental importance in theory and in practice. They can be used to form a classification of all coloured lights, which is simpler and more fundamental than that mentioned above because it refers only to three monochromatic lights and not to white light.

TRICHROMATIC SYSTEM OF CLASSIFICATION OF LIGHTS

It is easy to see that, in the same way as for the lights of the spectrum, any mixture of lights can be referred to a set of three primary lights, and can be characterized by coefficients similar to those that are given in Fig. 81 for monochromatic lights (6). The determination of the trichromatic coefficients corresponding to a light of any known spectral composition can be done by calculations, which have their foundation in the law of additivity of colour matches. In the case of the light reflected by a surface, the spectral energy distribution of this light, as has been seen, is a function of the spectral reflection curve of the surface and of the spectral energy distribution of the particular source of illumination. So that the trichromatic coefficients of the reflected light can be calculated knowing only the two latter sets of data.

When the light investigated is a mixed light—such as the light reflected by grass in sunshine—it often happens that it can be matched by a mixture of the three primaries placed all in the same half of the photometric field, the three coefficients being then, according to the convention given above, all positive. White light can be matched by a mixture of the three primaries of Fig. 81 in equal proportion, when the intensities of these primaries are expressed in the special units of the figure, which have been precisely chosen so as to give such a result. This, however, is true only for white light defined as the light of a particular artificial source. This light is different from, say, sunlight: it cannot give a perfect match with it. All varieties of " white " light can of course be characterized by their trichromatic coefficients.

For any given white light, it is possible to find a whole series of pairs of monochromatic lights which are complementary pairs. A mixture in suitable proportion of the lights of such a pair matches the white light. The wave-lengths of such complementaries again can be derived from the coefficient curves of Fig. 81. The first classification, mentioned above, of all lights in terms of white light and monochromatic or purple lights can also be derived quantitatively from the same curves, and can thus be reduced to the trichromatic system.

The characterization of all lights in the trichromatic system, that is, on the basis of their trichromatic coefficients, is often done with the help of a special diagram, the *colour triangle* or *chromaticity diagram* (6). This diagram, however, is nothing but a graphic method of representation. It merely expresses, in a way which has been found convenient in practice, the facts and relations described above.

The trichromatic system represents quantitatively the facts of colour mixture; it consists essentially of the data represented by the coefficient curves of Fig. 81, taken in conjunction with the law of additivity of colour matches. These experimental facts are thus of fundamental importance in the physiology of vision, but their validity is quite independent of any physiological theory of colour vision which may attempt to explain them.

These facts have taken a long time to establish accurately on account of technical difficulties. Many basic ideas had already been given by Newton, and were first developed by such physicists and physiologists as Maxwell and Helmholtz (9).

COLOUR VISION IN SMALL FOVEAL FIELDS

It is a remarkable fact that the properties of normal colour vision are quite different when a much smaller field, e.g. 20′ in diameter, falling in the middle of the fovea, is used instead of the field subtending 1° or 2° at the eye which gives the results described above. With such a small field the characteristics of colour vision correspond to a dichromatic system, similar to those which will be described in the next chapter in connexion with abnormal colour vision. All lights of the spectrum can here be matched by suitable mixtures of blue light and red light (10).

It has been recently found, moreover, that the same situation appears to exist also in small fields situated in other parts of the fovea—a fixation point being then used as in the experiments described in Figs. 35 and 36 of Chapter III. Quantitatively, if not qualitatively, the laws of colour mixture are found to be different in different parts of the fovea (7). How such an arrangement of apparently dichromatic foveal regions leads to the trichromatic vision described above when the whole fovea is covered by the image of a larger visual field, remains to be explained.

BIBLIOGRAPHY AND NOTES

(1) The possible use for analysing such lights of the effect of chromatic aberration in the eye really amounts to the use of a spectroscope and is not taken into consideration here.

(2) Extremely high intensities are avoided, however, for the laws of colour mixture break down under such conditions.

(3) KÖNIG, A. (1903). *Gesammelte Abhandlungen zur Physiologischen Optik*, 443 pp., Leipzig.

(4) GUILD, J. (1932). " The Colorimetric properties of the spectrum," *Phil. Trans. Roy. Soc. A.*, **230**, 149–187.

(5) This law would cease to be obeyed if all the matching wave-lengths had values very close to that of the original wave-length, but it is not meant to include such a peculiar case.

(6) WRIGHT, W. D. (1944). *The Measurement of Colour*, 223 pp., London.

(7) WRIGHT, W. D. (1946). *Researches on Normal and Defective Colour Vision*, 376 pp., London.

(8) RELATION BETWEEN DIFFERENT SETS OF TRICHROMATIC COEFFICIENT CURVES:

The quantitative relationship between all data obtained using different sets of primaries is due to the law of additivity of colour matches. It follows from this law that in any mixture of lights, a light or group of lights can be replaced by another light which matches it. It is true that as a rule there is no mixed light which matches a given monochromatic light of wave-length λ_1, but it has been seen (Fig. 81) that by adding another wave-length λ_0 to the given wave-length λ_1, this binary mixture of λ_0 and λ_1, can be matched by a mixture of two other mono-chromatic lights λ_2 and λ_3 (λ_1, λ_2 and λ_3 are the primaries 460, 530 and 650μ of Fig. 81). Now if any mixture A containing λ_1 matches another mixture B, it is possible to add first a certain amount of λ_0 to both A and B, thus obtaining two new mixtures A_1 and B_1 which give a colour match. If the amount of λ_0 is correctly chosen, it is then possible to replace the whole of the lights λ_0 and λ_1 in A_1 by the mixture of λ_2 and λ_3 which matches it. It is therefore possible to eliminate the light of wave-length λ_1 from the matching field, and still to have a new, perfect, match—involving now a new light λ_0.

In particular, suppose we want to obtain the coefficient curves similar to those of Fig. 81 but relating to a new, different set of three primaries. For any wave-length there exists a match involving the three old primaries in two binary mixtures;

this is the case, in particular, for the lights to be used as new primaries. For any λ as has just been explained, it is therefore possible, starting with a match involving the old primaries, to find a new match into which a new primary is introduced and in which one of the old primaries does not occur any more. By repetition of such a process a match can finally be obtained involving λ and the three new primaries only, which was the desired result.

All these complicated manipulations need not be carried out in actual experiments. Their final results, that is, the relative amounts of the various lights in the new pair of light mixtures giving a match, can be calculated directly from the data of Fig. 81. Such calculations, which are made using the so-called " colour equations ", give the same results as the experiments.

(9) The data are generally expressed in such a way that quantities of lights are not given in energy units as would appear most straightforward from the point of view of the physiologist, but in special luminosity units: this no doubt is partly due to the fact that most of the determinations were made primarily in view of practical problems of photometry and colorimetry.

(10) Willmer, E. N., and Wright, W. D. (1945). " Colour sensitivity of the fovea centralis," *Nature*, London, **156,** 119.

Chapter XIV

ABNORMAL COLOUR VISION

VARIETIES OF ABNORMAL COLOUR VISION

AMONG women 99·5 per cent., or more, have normal colour vision of the type described in the preceding section, but among men only about 92 per cent have normal colour vision (1). The persons who have abnormal colour vision—8 per cent. among men—can be divided into a number of classes. The larger number are *anomalous trichromats*: their colour vision presents the same general characteristics as that of trichromats (that is, the normal persons) but their trichromatic coefficient curves are of a different shape and their colour vision differs from that of the trichromats in certain other characteristics. Most of the others (2·6 per cent. among men) are *dichromats*: they can match any light with a mixture of two primary lights and thus differ fundamentally from the trichromats. An extremely small number (about 0·003 per cent. among men) are *monochromats*, that is, they are able to match any light with any other light, merely by adjusting the intensities.

In the case of monochromats, of course, one cannot speak of colour vision any more. There are two kinds of monochromats, namely, rod monochromats and cone monochromats. The rod monochromats have in their retina no cones, or at least no cones which respond to light. Their fovea is therefore blind and their maximum visual acuity is very poor. Their visibility curve at high intensities corresponds to the rod visibility curve obtained for normal persons at very low intensities of light. The vision of the cone monochromats differ less from normal vision than that of the rod monochromats; they have a high acuity and their visibility curve at high intensities is not a rod visibility curve (Fig. 82). While the rod monochromats have an obviously defective vision, the cone monochromats thus have a normal vision except of course for the striking fact that they can match any light with any other light. Cases of cone monochromatism are extremely rarely found.

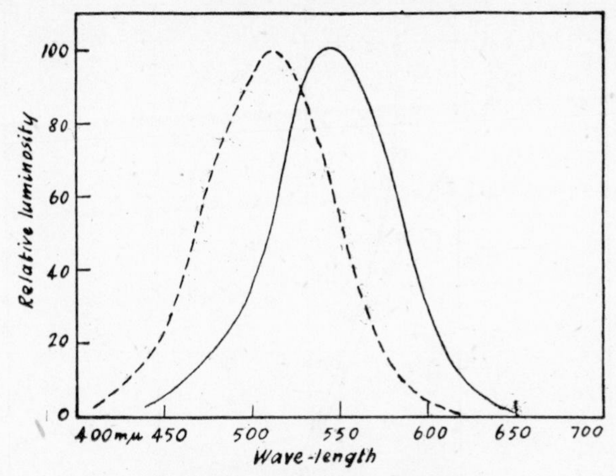

Fig. 82. Monochromatism.

Spectral sensitivity curve of a cone monochromat (full line) and of a rod monochromat (dotted line). The maxima of the two curves have been arbitrarily set at the same level. See text.

(After Pitt (2), *Nature*, **154**, 466, 1944.)

DICHROMATISM

This type of abnormal colour vision presents interesting characteristics. The complicated law of colour mixture of the trichromats is replaced in their case by the following simple law. Any light can be matched by a mixture of two monochromatic lights, taken from the two ends of the spectrum. This, for instance, is true of white light, and of course of any monochromatic light. Moreover, there is a monochromatic light of a certain wave-length which matches white light. White light can be replaced in a match by this particular wave-length without altering the match.

There are several types of dichromats (*protanopes*, *deuteranopes*, *tritanopes*) who differ, among other things, by the shape of their visibility curve. The visibility curve of dichromats is the same in kind as the visibility curve of trichromats; its maximum varies in position but is always found in the neighbourhood of 550mμ, that is, at wave-lengths which are definitely longer than the maximum of the rod visibility curve.

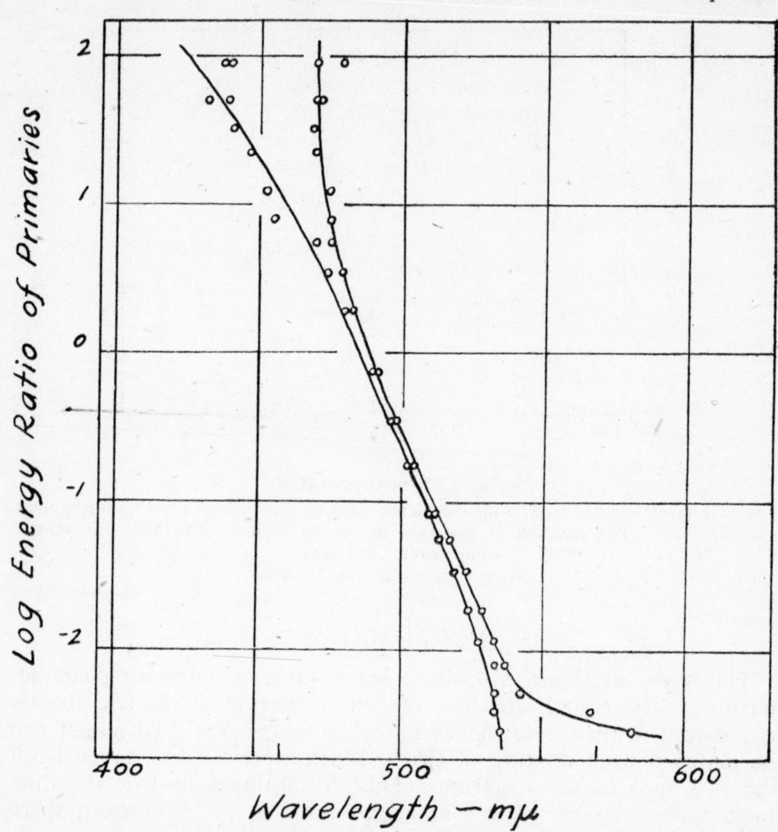

Fig. 83. Dichromatism.

Laws of " colour matching " for a protanope. The ordinates give the ratio of the amounts of energy of the two primaries, 458.7mμ and 570.0mμ (shown on the abscissa) which are matched by regions of the spectrum included between the experimental points. Light of $\lambda = 500$mμ, for instance, is matched by a mixture containing about 5 parts of 570 to 1 part of 458.7mμ.

(After Hecht and Shlaer (3), *J. Gen. Physiol.*, **20**, 57, 1936.)

Fig. 83 gives the experimental data relating to the matching of the spectral lights with two primaries by a protanope, whose visibility curve (not reproduced here) is very similar to the visibility curve of the cone monochromat, given in Fig. 82. This protanope has a neutral point at 491·6mμ, that is, light of this wave-length matches white light. By mixing white light, or light of 491·6mμ, with light of the blue end of the spectrum, all spectral lights from the blue end to 491·6mμ can be matched. Similarly, lights belonging to the part of the spectrum extending from 491·6mμ to the red end can be matched with white light, or 491·6mμ, plus light of the red end of the spectrum (3). Monochromatic lights of different wave-lengths thus do not appear identical to such a dichromat, at least in the middle of the spectrum (for the discrimination between wave-lengths is very poor at the ends of the spectrum).

Dichromats sometimes confuse colours such as that of the fruit and leaves of a cherry tree. If the lights reflected by the cherries and the leaves were pure monochromatic lights belonging respectively to the red and to the green part of the spectrum, they should appear different to the dichromat, according to the above. These lights, however, are not monochromatic, and it may happen that, for the dichromats, these two different compound lights can be both matched by the same mixture of white light with light from the red end of the spectrum. The light reflected by the cherries and the light reflected by the leaves, therefore, may appear identical to the dichromat. Even if they are not quite indistinguishable, however, they are likely to appear as two mixtures of white with red light, one of the mixture containing a larger proportion of red. It is understandable then that the dichromat will more readily fail to notice the cherries among the leaves, than an observer having normal vision.

OBJECTIVITY OF THESE STUDIES OF COLOUR VISION

It will be noted that in all the experiments described in this chapter, and in the preceding one, the human subject of the experiment is required only to indicate whether the two halves of the photometric field appear identical to him, or not. If reference to the subject's sensations is made, it may be said that the experiment shows whether the two sensations produced by the two halves of the field are the same or not; but in any case there is no reference to the actual *nature* of the subject's sensations. Furthermore, it is also possible to describe the experiment simply by saying that the subject *responds* in an identical, or a different, manner to the lights emitted by the two halves of the field. Discussion of the psychology of sensation can thus be avoided.

While we do not learn from it anything about sensations as such, therefore, the present method of approach makes possible a purely objective study of the physiological response of the organism to light. Accordingly, there is no theoretical difficulty in applying the same method to the study of vision in animals—about whose sensations we could not hope to gain accurate information. And it becomes clear why quantitative calculations can be made in the investigation of colour vision, which from a certain point of view appears to be a problem of such a subjective nature. The calculations and classifications all refer to lights, that is, to objective physical stimuli only.

It has been demonstrated that the honey-bee is capable of discriminating between some of the wave-lengths of the spectrum, independently of the intensity of the light. This was achieved by using the same kind of training method as that mentioned in Chapter IX, which showed that the bee can discriminate between a black circle and a cross. The bee can be trained to come to a blue paper surrounded by many grey papers of various shades. In a similar way it has been found that the bee is sensitive to ultra-violet radiation between 400 and 310 mμ, which it discriminates from the rest of the spectrum. This radiation is reflected by some flowers in sunlight (4).

BIBLIOGRAPHY

(1) For the percentage values in this paragraph, see ref. (7) of preceding chapter.

(2) Pitt, F. H. G. (1944). "Monochromatism," *Nature*, Lond., **154,** 466.

(3) Hecht, S., and Shlaer, S. (1936). "The color vision of dichromats," *J. Gen. Physiology*, **20,** 57–93.

(4) For a review of our knowledge of the colour vision of animals, see Buddenbrock, W. von (1937). *Grundriss der vergleichenden Physiologie*, 2d. ed., 2 vol., Berlin.

Piéron, H. (1941). *Psychologie Zoologique*, Paris.

Chapter XV

THOMAS YOUNG'S THEORY OF COLOUR VISION

OBJECT OF THE THEORY

A physiological theory of colour vision must explain, first of all, how and why the organism gives qualitatively different responses to certain lights having different physical compositions. Lights of, say, 400 mμ and 500 mμ appear different to the eye and this difference cannot be eliminated by changes of intensity—while in the case of the action of light upon an ordinary photographic plate, for instance, all lights produce the same kind of effect. Furthermore a complete theory should explain quantitatively, among many other things, the facts of "colour matching". That is, it should explain why certain lights having very different physical composition nevertheless produce identical responses in the organism.

A SINGLE RECEPTOR RESPONDS IN THE SAME WAY TO ALL WAVE-LENGTHS

In the simple case of a single optic nerve fibre of the eye of *Limulus*, especially clear evidence has been obtained, showing that the nature of the nervous response is independent of the wave-length of the stimulating light. For by the proper adjustment of intensities, responses can be obtained which are identical, impulse for impulse, as closely as the reproducibility of the results will allow, for all the spectral lights used (1). Moreover, the ratios of the intensities for the various wave-lengths necessary to produce a constant response do not vary with the intensity level of the stimulating light; there is no effect similar to the Purkinje phenomenon. Thus, like an ordinary photographic plate, a system constituted of such a fibre with its attached sense-cell is incapable of discriminating between lights of different wave-lengths.

VISION OF THE MONOCHROMAT

All the available evidence tends to show that the ordinary laws of nervous action (examined in Chapter V) apply to the optic nerve fibres which are connected to the retinal receptors responsible for colour vision. If this is so, it follows that when the receptors have all the same sensitivity in the spectrum, there cannot be any qualitatively different response to lights of different wave-lengths. Consider, for instance, the case of a rod monochromat whose retina contains rods only, or consider the case of a normal individual at such low light intensities that no cone is functioning. When any light falls on the rods (Fig. 84)

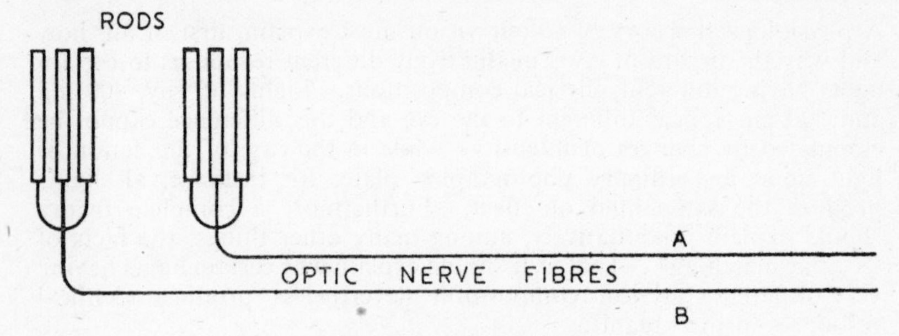

Fig. 84. (Schematic.)

it stimulates them to an extent determined by the light intensity *and* by the sensitivity of the rods to this particular light. As in the case of a single photo-receptor of *Limulus*, the final stimulation in the nerve fibre will be the same if a small amount of light of, say, 500 mμ, to which the rods are very sensitive, is used, or if a larger amount of light of 600 mμ, to which the rods are less sensitive, is used. Moreover, if two neighbouring groups of rods receive the same light, the stimulation will vary in the same way in the two fibres A and B connected to each group of rods; if the light stimulates strongly fibre A it also stimulates strongly fibre B (only one type of fibre, for instance " ordinary fibres ", is of course considered at a time). This makes it clear that any state of stimulation of a fibre may be obtained using any kind of light, and that comparison of the stimulation produced in neighbouring fibres is unable to reveal anything about the wave-length of the stimulating light. The organism cannot respond in a specific manner to the wave-length of the light.

Let us now consider a cone connected to its nerve fibre. Suggestions of the following kind are sometimes made concerning the functioning of such a unit, but they are purely *ad hoc* hypotheses, unsupported by physiological evidence. It is suggested that the discharge of impulses in the nerve fibre has a different character according to the wavelength of the light which stimulates the cone. Each region of the spectrum would, for instance, be characterized by a special arrangement in the successive impulses, rather in the same way as different letters are transmitted on a single telegraphic wire using the Morse code. Such suggestions are mentioned here because they are not uncommon. Sometimes they are made tacitly, as in theories of colour vision which deal only with the action of light on chemical substances in the retina, without further reference to the nervous system of which the retina is a part. Opinions of this kind will be disregarded here, because there is no evidence showing that optic nerve fibres behave in such a way.

Now if we suppose that the cones of the cone monochromat have all the same spectral sensitivity—and that their nerve fibres, of course, behave as ordinary nerve fibres—this hypothesis at once explains the characteristics of the vision of the rod-free area of the monochromat; this case then is similar to that of the rod monochromat. This hypothesis is not necessarily the only explanation, however, as will be seen presently.

It must be remarked here that the cone monochromat possesses no colour vision at all, even in regions of his retina which contain both rods and cones. The parafovea, for instance, contains presumably both rods and cones. These have different physiological properties, among which must be counted the spectral sensitivity curves, for the sensitivity curve of the cones of the cone monochromat is very different from the rod visibility curve (Fig. 82 of preceding chapter). The case of the cone monochromat thus is a *prima facie* case showing that the co-existence of two kinds of receptors having different spectral sensitivities is not a *sufficient* condition for the existence of colour vision.

There is no logical impossibility about this. Let us imagine, for instance, that at any level in the nervous system the fibres coming from the cones and from the rods belonging to a point of the retina of the monochromat, converge onto a single nerve fibre (Fig. 85). This fibre reacts according to the general laws of nervous action, and makes connexions with the motor centres which put the muscles into action. It is clear that, if there is no branching-off from the nerve fibres before their fusion, the muscles of the organism cannot respond in a qualitatively different manner to the stimulation of the rods and cones in various ratios. Even in the extreme cases in which rods alone, or cones alone, are stimulated, there is no difference in the kind of stimulation produced in the final common path leading to the muscles. Thus the organism cannot respond differently to lights of different wave-lengths, although these lights stimulate rods and cones in different ratios.

The mere possibility of such an imaginary arrangement is enough to prove that different kinds of stimulation can be produced in the retinal receptors by different lights, and yet that this difference may be lost, so to speak, at some subsequent level in the nervous system. If the qualitative difference between two kinds of stimulation vanishes entirely in such a way at some level in the nervous system, it is obvious that it cannot be created again by any subsequent nervous process.

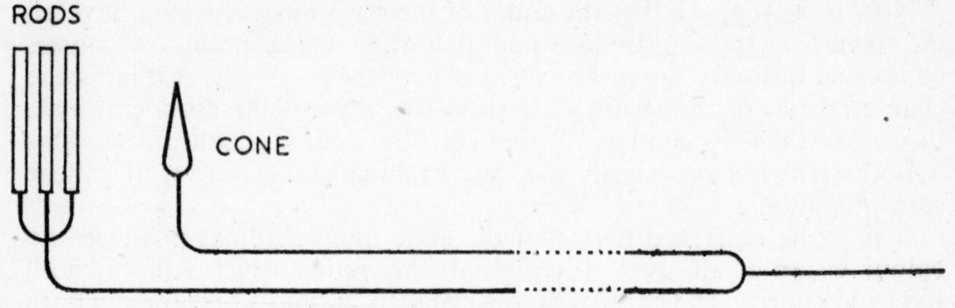

Fig. 85. (Schematic.)

It follows from all this that there might logically be cones having various spectral sensitivities in the retina of the cone monochromat, if some special arrangement in the nervous connexions exists. Such a complicated situation is not very likely *a priori* because the high acuity of cone monochromats gives support to the view that there is a one-to-one connexion of the cones to the nerve fibres, while it appears that an arrangement on the lines suggested above would amount to the loss of such a one-to-one relationship at some level in the nervous system.

In conclusion, when all the receptors of the retina have the same spectral sensitivity, there can be no colour vision. When the retina contains receptors having different spectral sensitivities, colour vision is possible but is not always present. The existence of several such kinds of receptors is necessary for colour vision, but it is not by itself a sufficient condition.

VISION OF THE DICHROMAT

Let us now imagine that a point of the retina contains two cones A and B (Fig. 86). Each cone is sensitive to the whole spectrum, but each has a spectral sensitivity curve of a different shape as shown in Fig. 87. In such a case, light of any wave-length falling on these two cones stimulates both of them, A and B, but it generally stimulates A and B to different extents. Light of another wave-length will produce another ratio of stimulations in cone A and cone B. Light of wave-length λ_1 will, for instance, stimulate cone A to a greater extent than cone B, while wave-length λ_2 will stimulate cone A less than cone B. And in whatever way the intensity of the light is chosen, this difference will subsist (except at such high intensities that the response of both A and B is always maximal). Such a system would thus respond in qualitatively different ways to lights of different wave-lengths.

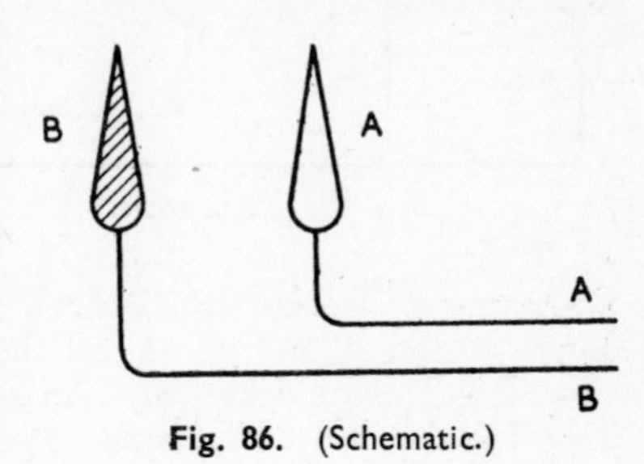

Fig. 86. (Schematic.)

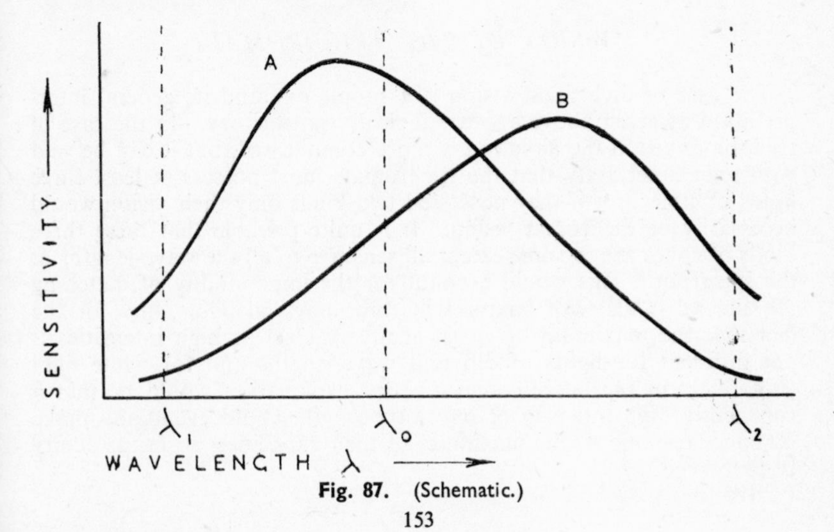

Fig. 87. (Schematic.)

Moreover, it should be possible by mixing lights λ_1 and λ_2 of the two ends of the spectrum to stimulate the two cones A and B exactly in the same way as they would be stimulated by an intermediate wave-length λ_0. Such an arrangement of receptors would thus, first, respond differently to certain different lights and, secondly, give an identical response to certain other lights notwithstanding that they are physically different. It is apparent that such a system would correspond in all its main characteristic to a dichromat visual system.

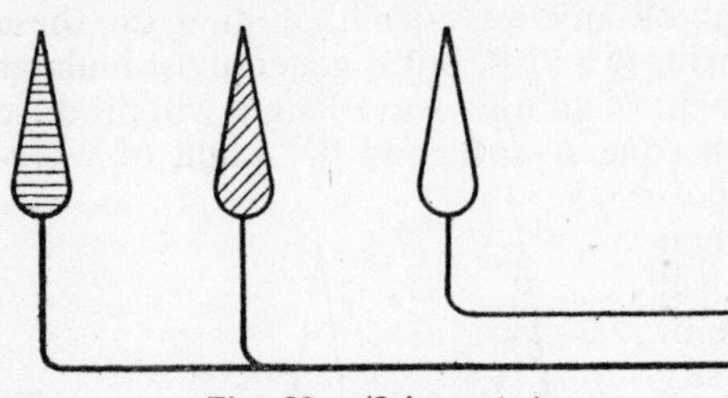

Fig. 88. (Schematic.)

It will be noted again that if such a fusion as that of Fig. 85 (without any branching-off) occurred between the fibres coming from the two cones A and B of Fig. 86, all the power of discrimination between wave-lengths would be lost. An arrangement of three different cones as in Fig. 88, however, might again act as a dichromat system.

VISION OF THE TRICHROMAT

The case of dichromat vision is a simple one and its general interpretation as given above appears logically satisfactory. In the case of trichromat vision the situation is more complicated, but it can be said with logical certainty that the trichromats must possess at least three kinds of cones, for if they possessed two kinds only their vision would necessarily be dichromat vision. It is quite possible that these three kinds of cones are to some extent all sensitive to all the wave-lengths of the spectrum. This would account for the impossibility of matching all spectral lights with mixtures of three physical lights, and for the fact that the maximum of visual acuity reached at high intensities is not different for lights of different wave-lengths and for white light (Fig. 70). In the latter connexion, the explanation would be that a sufficiently high intensity of *any* wave-length would eventually make *all* cones respond to the maximum of their capacities, so far as acuity is concerned.

THOMAS YOUNG'S THEORY

The ideas expressed above have their origin in some concise suggestions made by Thomas Young in 1801 (2). These did not make any impression until Helmholtz, reading Young's paper some fifty years later, adopted them with enthusiasm as the key to the problem of colour vision (3). It appears that Thomas Young foresaw something similar to the modern doctrine of nervous action, according to which each nerve fibre can transmit only one kind of sensory " message ". This at first seemed to lead him to the conclusion that there must be as many different kinds of receptors as there are colours; but as he says, " it becomes necessary to suppose the number limited; for instance, to the three principal colours, red, yellow and blue, . . ." (2). For the abnormal colour vision of such persons as his contemporary Dalton, Young himself suggested as an explanation " the absence or paralysis of those fibres of the retina which are calculated to perceive red " (4).

It does not seem admissible to consider these conceptions as forming merely a possible physiological theory of colour vision, among other possible, but radically different, theories. For the present method of approach really rests on the two following principles, taken in conjunction with the laws of action of nerve fibres. First, if two different physical lights are able to produce two qualitatively different responses in the organism, a difference in nervous stimulation must already exist in the receptors of the retina, and subsist to a significant extent throughout the relevant parts of the nervous system. Secondly, if two different physical lights produce the same final response in the organism, they must, at some level of the nervous system, produce stimulations which are qualitatively the same. (By qualitative differences it is meant differences such as have been discussed above in relation with Fig. 87.)

These principles appear inescapable, when the organism is considered as a kind of mechanism in the most general sense of the word. And refusing to consider the organism as a mechanism amounts to rejecting the physiological method of approach. It follows from these two principles that the whole nervous system must be considered as one single functional whole. Arguments about whether colour vision is a function purely of the retina, or of the brain, appear meaningless. If discrimination between lights is not made by the retina it will not be made at all. And if a significant difference in stimulation, related to a difference of light stimuli, is found at any nervous level, say, in the brain, it must be possible to trace it backwards to the retina.

Measurements of the amount of light energy of various wave-lengths necessary to obtain a threshold discharge in single optic nerve fibres of various vertebrates, such as the frog and the snake, have recently been made using a method related to that used above in the case of *Limulus* (5). Different types of spectral sensitivity curves corresponding to different nerve fibres have been found in that way. Besides the broad rod curve, other types of sensitivity curves, broad and narrow, have been obtained. According to the animal, the number of different types of curves varies, being sometimes more, sometimes less, than three. These findings appear to constitute direct experimental evidence for Thomas Young's general assumption of a " limited number " of types of photo-receptors. The curves obtained, however, do not always necessarily represent the sensitivity curves of the individual receptors, the anatomical and physiological arrangements being here much more complex than in the case of *Limulus*.

CONES AND RODS IN COLOUR VISION

Only cones have been considered in the above reasonings to take part in the mechanism of colour vision. The main justification of this is that colour vision is generally observed to exist under conditions where cones, or mostly cones, are stimulated, while vision is colourless where rods alone are stimulated. In the experiment of Chapter III, for instance, in which small areas of the fovea and parafovea were stimulated using blue and red light, it has been found that, for blue light, the light is seen coloured in the rod-free area while it appears colourless in areas containing a fair number of rods. For red light, the presence or absence of rods has little influence on the colour of the light in the regions shown on Fig. 36, but the light appears orange, and then colourless, in regions containing many rods. Under these conditions, it can be concluded, therefore, that the rod-free area is the best region for colour vision; the presence of rods seems to have only detrimental effects. This however refers to conditions of dark adaptation and it might be argued that rods are necessary for colour vision at high intensities. In that case the rod-free fovea should not have the same colour vision at high intensities as a larger field which covers rod-containing regions of the parafovea. (According to Fig. 37, the field 2^0 in diameter often used e.g. in the determination of trichromatic coefficient curves would contain a certain number of rods.) There does not seem to be any evidence that entirely rod-free fields have different colour vision, however. Again, the case of the cone monochromat, already discussed, is an argument against the theory that rods can be one of the colour receptors. For if they were so, one would expect these monochromats, who have both rods and cones in their retina, to have dichromat, instead of monochromat, vision (6).

PROPERTIES OF THE CONES

Logical deductions thus lead to the idea that there must exist more than one kind of cone in the fovea, presumably three kinds, in the fovea of the trichromat. It has not been possible, however, to see under the microscope several kinds of cones corresponding to these theoretical expectations. This is not really surprising and is no argument against the theory, for the following reasons. The only essential difference which must exist between the various cones is one of spectral sensitivity. This in turn is very probably due to the presence in the cones of pigments sensitive to light which have different absorption spectra in different kinds of cones. These pigments should then give different colorations to the different cones. Now the reason why such differences of coloration have not been seen is simply that the coloration itself is probably undetectable by the eye. The concentration of the pigments sensitive to light in the cones is probably very low. In contra-distinction to the case of visual purple in the rods, it has not been possible to extract and purify these cone substances (7). Furthermore, these substances must be expected to be rapidly bleached by the light used to see the cones under the microscope.

Many attempts have been made to derive the spectral sensitivity curves of the three kinds of cones from the experimental data of colour vision. The reasonings used are not always easy to follow, and it may perhaps be questioned whether our knowledge of the physiological mechanisms involved is sufficient as a basis for such calculations. For we do not know how the various nerve fibres coming from the colour receptors are connected in the cerebral cortex, or how their various excitations interact, there, if they do so. If we knew with certainty the laws of action of the nervous structures concerned with colour vision, we should be able to derive from the experimental data of colour vision such characteristics as the spectral sensitivities of the various kinds of cones. These laws of action, however, have to be replaced by assumptions. This may well be the cause of the variety of theoretical sensitivity curves which have been suggested (8). The complexities revealed by the peculiar colour vision of very small fields, mentioned in Chapter XIII, must also be borne in mind in this connexion.

It is nevertheless worth mentioning here, although it cannot be examined in detail, a particular derivation leading to three broad sensitivity curves, overlapping over the whole spectrum, which may be assumed to correspond to the types of cones determining the response of a fairly large foveal field (9). These three curves are derived from measurements which are completely independent of the data of colour-matching. Using only some other simple data and assumptions based on experimental results, it is then possible to calculate, on the basis of these three curves, whether two physical lights will be indistinguishable to the eye, or not—both from the point of view of " colour " and of " brightness " (10). This very general problem includes, of course, as a particular case, the laws of colour-matching of Fig. 81. The agreement between this scheme, which uses no gratuitous assumptions, and so many experimental data, gives confidence in its validity.

BIBLIOGRAPHY AND NOTES

(1) GRAHAM, C. H., and HARTLINE, H. K. (1935). " The response of single visual sense cells to lights of different wave-lengths," *J. Gen. Physiol.*, **18**, 917–931.

(2) YOUNG, T. (1802). " On the Theory of Light and Colours," *Phil. Trans. Roy. Soc.*, Part 1, 20. Reprinted in *Lectures on Natural Philosophy*, 1st. ed., vol. 2, p. 613 (London, 1807). It may be of historical interest to reproduce here Young's brief statement of his theory, although he put it in a form very different from that which might be used today:—

" . . . Now, as it is almost impossible to conceive each sensitive point of the retina to contain an infinite number of particles, each capable of vibrating in perfect unison with every possible undulation, it becomes necessary to suppose the number limited; for instance, to the three principal colours, red, yellow, and blue, of which the undulations are related in magnitude nearly as the numbers 8, 7, and 6; and that each of the particles is capable of being put in motion less or more forcibly, by undulations differing less or more from a perfect unison; for instance, the undulations of green light, being nearly in the ratio of 6½, will affect equally the particles in unison with yellow and blue, and produce the same effect as a light composed of those two species: and each sensitive filament of the nerve may consist of three portions, one for each principal colour . . ."

(3) HECHT, S. (1930). "The development of Thomas Young's theory of colour vision," *J. Opt. Soc. Amer.*, **20**, 231.
See also MILLINGTON, E. C. (1942). "History of the Young-Helmholtz theory of colour vision," *Ann. of Sc.*, **5**, 167.

(4) YOUNG, T. (1807). Note on a paper by Dalton in the "Catalogue" in *Lectures on Natural Philosophy*, 1st ed., vol. 2, p. 315, London.
This note reads:—

"Dalton on some facts relating to the vision of colours. *Manch. M.*, V. 28.

His own case, agreeing with those of several other persons. He cannot distinguish blue from pink by daylight, but by candlelight the pink appears red; in the solar spectrum the red is scarcely visible; the rest appears to consist of two colours, yellow and blue, or of yellow, blue, and purple. He thinks it probable that the vitreous humour is of a deep blue tinge: but this has never been observed by anatomists, and it is much more simple to suppose the absence or paralysis of those fibres of the retina, which are calculated to perceive red; this supposition explains all the phenomena, except that greens appear to become bluish when viewed by candlelight; but in this circumstance there is perhaps no great singularity."

(5) GRANIT, R. (1947), *Sensory Mechanisms of the Retina, with an Appendix on Electroretinography*. Oxford.

(6) The opposite view, i.e. that the rods are one of the colour receptors, is taken in:
WILLMER, E. N. (1946). *Retinal Structure and Colour Vision, A Restatement and an Hypothesis*. Cambridge.

(7) HECHT, S. (1942). "The Chemistry of visual substances," *Annual Review of Biochemistry*, XI.

(8) Moreover, it cannot be denied that this field is sometimes obscured by confusions. The spectral sensitivity curves of the cones clearly must be defined in the usual physiological way (cf. Chapter IV). That is, they must give for each wave-length the reciprocal of the light energy which must fall on the cone in order to elicit

a given, constant, response in the cone. It is evident that the light energy striking the cone must be positive. It is not possible to understand the meaning of a negative amount of energy striking the cone, unless (by analogy with a body which, in physics, is sometimes said to absorb a negative amount of heat when it actually emits heat), it is that the cone actually throws light out of the retina when it gives a nervous impulse—a striking absurdity. Curves which purport to represent the spectral sensitivity of the cones are nevertheless sometimes published having negative values for certain wave-lengths. It should be clear that such curves cannot really be cone sensitivity curves in the above meaning; it seems that they generally are modifications of the coefficient curves of Fig. 81, which have a well-defined, but quite different, physiological meaning.

(9) Stiles, W. S. (1939). "The directional sensitivity of the retina and the spectral sensitivities of the rods and cones," *Proc. Roy. Soc.*, B, **127,** 64–105.

(10) Stiles, W. S. (1946). "A modified Helmholtz line-element in brightness-colour space," *Proc. Phys. Soc. Lond.*, **58**, 41–65. See also, ref. (2) of Chapter VIII, and the Proceedings, to be published, of the International Colour-Vision Conference held in Cambridge in 1947.

Chapter XVI

THE TWO EYES AND THE BRAIN

UNIOCULAR ESTIMATION OF DISTANCE

OUR estimation of the distance and relief of objects is very imperfect when, without extraneous clues to help us, we use only one eye, and do not move our head. The clues which usually help us are: the effects of linear perspective or the apparent shape and size of familiar objects such as men or houses, and the effects of aerial perspective, which is the change in the apparent coloration of distant objects caused by the layer of air interposed between them and the eye. The practice of painting is based upon the use of these two kinds of perspective.

The uncertainty of one eye in judging depth and relative distance is well brought out by many laboratory experiments. One such simple experiment consists in looking through an eye-piece with one eye at an array of vertical black threads placed in front of a white background, in an attempt to judge the relative distance of the threads from the eye, or to say which one lies behind the other. Considerable uncertainty and error is found in trying to make such judgments, which become practically impossible at ten metres (1).

Such distance determination rests on the mechanism of accommodation of the eye, whereby the lens becomes more or less convex in shape, according as the object is nearer to or farther from the eye, in order to keep its image accurately focussed on the retina.

If one looks at the foliage of trees in a thick wood, using only one eye and keeping the head immobile, it is very difficult to make out the relative positions of the many twigs and leaves which one sees, for the reason given above. But if the eye is moved by displacing the head, the relief at once becomes much clearer. And if the two eyes are used in the ordinary way, the disposition in space of the objects seen regains its usual clearness.

When the eye is displaced, the images of objects situated at different distances are displaced to different extents on the retina. As shown in Fig. 89, when the eye is in position 1, the nearer object A appears on the right of the farther object B, while A appears on the left of B when the eye is moved to position 2. Such changes in apparent position make it possible for an observer to say that B is situated behind A.

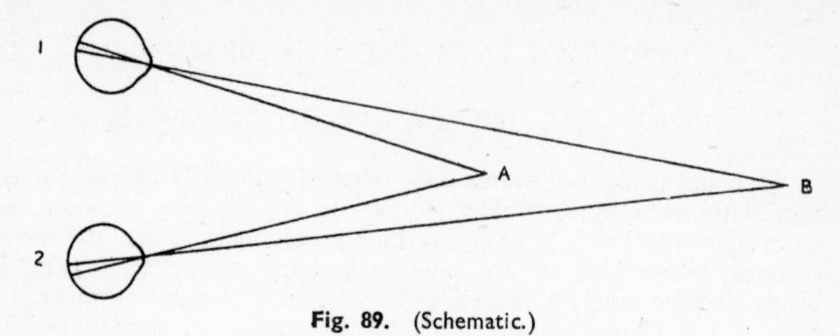

Fig. 89. (Schematic.)

STEREOSCOPIC VISION

Similarly, in the use of both eyes in ordinary binocular vision, the estimation of distances (or what is sometimes called " the perception of a third dimension ") is due to the fact that the images formed on the two retinae are not quite the same. In Fig. 89 the two positions of one eye at 1 and 2 might just as well represent the positions of both eyes of one individual.

We may here refer again to Leonardo's Window. The perspective image of the cube on the sheet of glass, as shown in Fig. 15 of Chapter I, is drawn for one of the two eyes. Since the other eye of the observer is in a different position in space, it is clear that another " pyramid of sight " corresponds to this second eye. Its intersection with the pane of glass determines another, different, perspective image. Thus the retinal images of the cube are different for the two eyes. The perspective image corresponding to the second eye is not given in the figure, but one can illustrate the point for oneself simply by looking through the window into the street. If the two eyes are shut alternately, it will be observed that the objects outside change noticeably their apparent disposition with reference to one another, and with reference to any fixed point on the window pane.

As Leonardo knew, therefore, it is not possible to make a painting which gives a perfect illusion of depth when it is seen binocularly. It may be noted, however, that a very good illusion of depth may be obtained when one eye only is used, because in that case, as we have already seen, the estimation of depth is very poor. This fact lies at the foundation of the theory of representation in painting or photography.

It is possible, with the help of special arrangements, to present separately to each eye a different picture or photograph. The stereoscope achieves this by means of mirrors or prisms. In the method of anaglyphs, which is perhaps the simplest in principle, the perspective images corresponding to the two eyes are drawn on the same sheet of

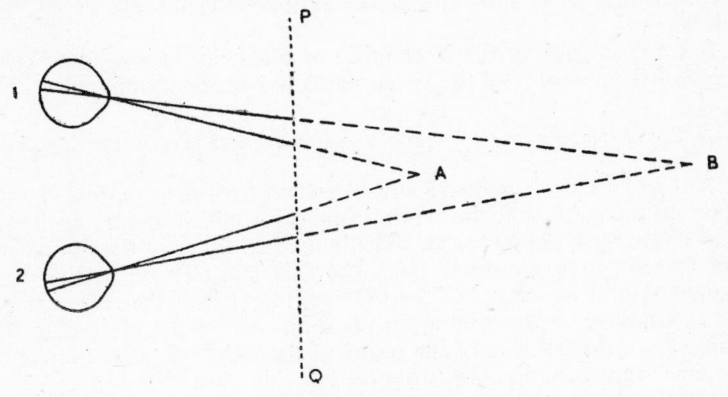

Fig. 90. (Schematic.)

paper, each in a different colour. Two specially selected glasses of different colours are placed in front of the eyes. In this way the picture seen by the left eye is rendered invisible to the right, and vice versa. If the two perspective images have been suitably prepared, the effect of the stimulation of the two retinae will be the same as if they were both stimulated normally by the same set of objects in space. In the case of Fig. 90 the images formed in the two eyes looking at the two pairs of points on the plane PQ are the same as if two points A and B were placed one behind the other, in front of the eyes.

When we look at a given point of an object, the eyes converge or diverge, as the case may be, in order to bring the image of this point on to the fovea of each eye at the same time. The degree of convergence varies inversely with the distance of the object. For very distant objects, such as stars, the lines of sight, which pass through the fovea and posterior nodal point, are parallel. When the retinal images of an object fall in this way on the fovea of each retina, the object is seen as one, single, individual thing. Objects situated at other distances, for which the degree of convergence of the eyes is not therefore correct, appear as two objects. With a little practice one can become aware of these other objects. For instance, hold the two index fingers, one behind the other about one foot apart at the level of the eyes. Now if you look at the nearer finger, two blurred images of the other can be seen. Similarly, if you look at the farther one, the nearer is " seen double ".

For a discussion of the mechanism of binocular vision, some knowledge of the anatomy of the visual paths is a necessary pre-requisite.

HOW THE RETINAE ARE CONNECTED TO THE BRAIN

We have seen in Chapter I, on the structure of the eye, that the two optic nerves unite to form the optic chiasma, which divides again into the two diverging optic tracts. The individual fibres of the optic nerve run without interruption through the chiasma. Those coming from the left side of the retina of the left eye, turn left at the chiasma, into the left optic tract, remaining on the same side of the brain (Fig. 91). Those from the left side of the retina of the right eye cross over at the chiasma, and with the fibres from the left side of the left eye, also enter the left optic tract. Thus the left optic tract is constituted of fibres originating from the left side of each of the retinae. In a similar way, the right optic tract contains the fibres belonging to the right sides of the two retinae. (This arrangement is not found in all animals. In some, all the fibres from the left eye cross over to the right at the chiasma, while all those from the right cross over to the left.) At the end of the optic tracts *t*, the fibres enter the *lateral geniculate bodies l.* In these bodies each fibre ends, connecting up with new fibres which constitute the *optic radiation r* of the brain. There is no cross connection or overlapping in the lateral geniculate bodies, so that the paths corresponding to each optic nerve fibre remain separated in the optic radiation. The fibres of the optic radiation eventually reach a part of the cerebral cortex at the back of the head, called the *striate area* or *field* 17.

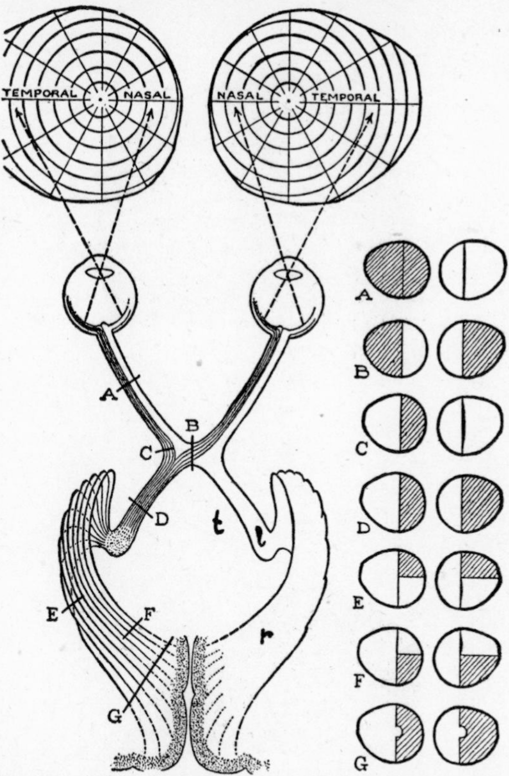

Fig. 91. Optic pathways and visual fields in man.
Diagram showing the effects on the fields of vision produced by lesions at various points along the optic pathways. See text.
(From J. Homans, *A Textbook of Surgery*, C. C. Thomas, Springfield, Ill., 1945 (2).)

EFFECTS OF INJURIES TO THE VISUAL PATHS

If one of the optic nerves is severed, the corresponding eye becomes totally blind, because no nervous stimulation can then reach the brain from its retina. Now according to the anatomical arrangements just observed, it is only to be expected that if, say, the left optic tract is entirely severed, the left sides of both retinae will for a similar reason

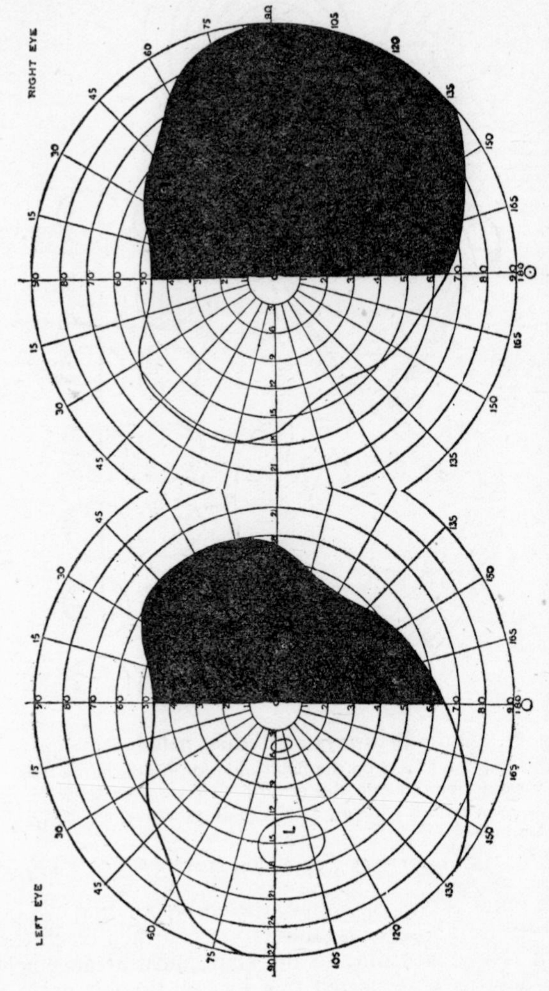

Fig. 92. Blindness of the right halves of the fields of vision, due to destruction of the left striate area.

(From Holmes (3), *Proc. Roy. Soc.* B, 132, 348, 1945.)

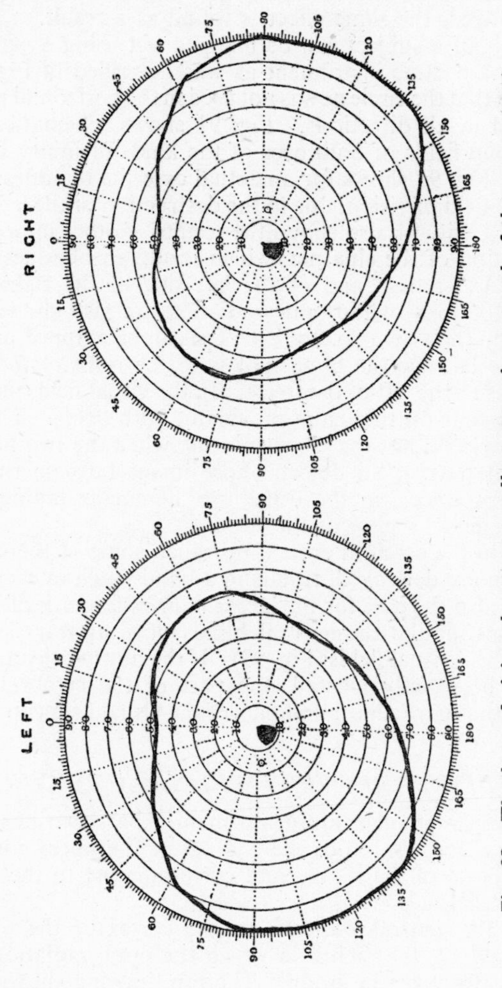

Fig. 93. The loss of vision due to a small penetrating wound of the upper part of the posterior portion of the striate area of the right side.

The blind areas remained unaltered for more than four years after the infliction of the wound.

(From Holmes (3), *Proc. Roy. Soc.* B, **132**, 348, 1945.

become blind. This is in fact found to be the case when this kind of injury occurs in man. And if the entire optic radiation of one side of the brain is destroyed, the same effect is found as a result.

The visual fields of a subject can be mapped out using a perimeter; this is essentially the same instrument as was described in Fig. 39 of Chapter III except that the circle now is not used in the horizontal position only, but is tilted in all directions. Fig. 91 shows schematically the effects on the visual fields of both eyes of the kinds of injury we have been describing. Fig. 92 shows for an actual case the blindness of the right halves of the field of vision, due to the destruction of the left striate area of the cortex. Fig. 91 also shows the results of other injuries such as the medial section of the chiasma, which results in blindness of the right side of the left retina, and of the left side of the right retina. Results of partial lesions of the optic radiation are also shown (4).

The blind spot in the visual field of each eye can be mapped using the perimeter. In the left eye the blind spot is to the right of the fovea; in the right eye it is to the left of the fovea. In the visual field, therefore, the blind spots appear on the temporal side in both fields. The blind spots of the two eyes do not therefore coincide when the two fields are superposed. That part of an object whose image falls on the blind spot of one eye produces, in the other eye, an image falling on an ordinary (or " seeing ") region of the retina.

A small injury in the cerebral cortex, by which some of the fibres of the optic radiation are destroyed, results in a blind patch in each of the visual fields, as is also the case for the larger injuries E and F of Fig. 91. Such blind patches, unlike the natural blinds pots, appear on corresponding parts of the visual fields (Fig. 93). If the injury causing such a blind patch can be exactly located, the part of the cerebral cortex corresponding to that particular blind part of the visual field can thereby be identified.

CORRESPONDENCE BETWEEN RETINA AND CORTEX

By prolonged study of such injuries in man, it has been possible to map on the cortex the position of the endings of the fibres connected with the various parts of the retina, and corresponding to the various parts of the visual field (3).

Fig. 94 shows the general position on the cortex of the so-called *striate area*, or *field* 17, the region in which the optic radiation fibres end in each hemisphere of the brain. The top drawing shows a part of this striate area at the tip of the occipital cortex of the left hemisphere as seen from the outside of the intact brain; the eyes, if drawn, would be on the left of the illustration. The lower drawing shows the part of the striate area which is seen on the right cerebral hemisphere when the left hemisphere, shown in the upper drawing, is removed. Most of the

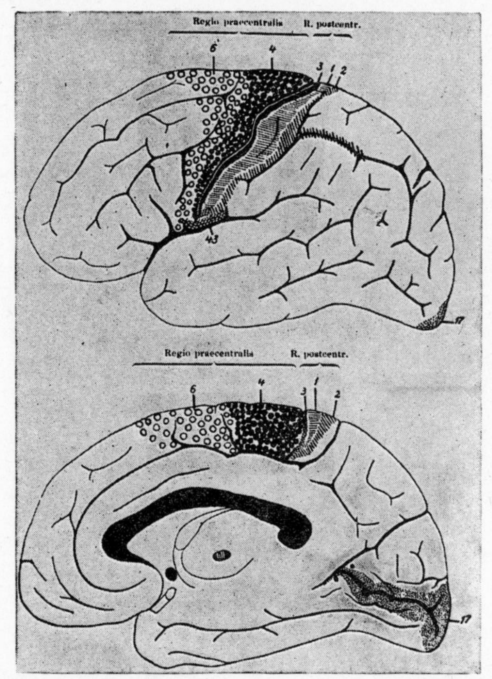

Fig. 94. The position of the visual cortex in man.

The striate area, or field 17, is seen on the right. A large part of it is buried in the calcarine fissure. See text.

(From Holmes (3), *Proc. Roy. Soc.* B, **132**, 348, 1945.)

visual cortex is thus located at the surface of the deep fissure separating the two cerebral hemispheres. This is also shown in the schema of Fig. 91. In both hemispheres, again, a large part of the striate area is buried in one of the fissures of the cortex itself, the *calcarine fissure*, as shown in the lower illustration of Fig. 94.

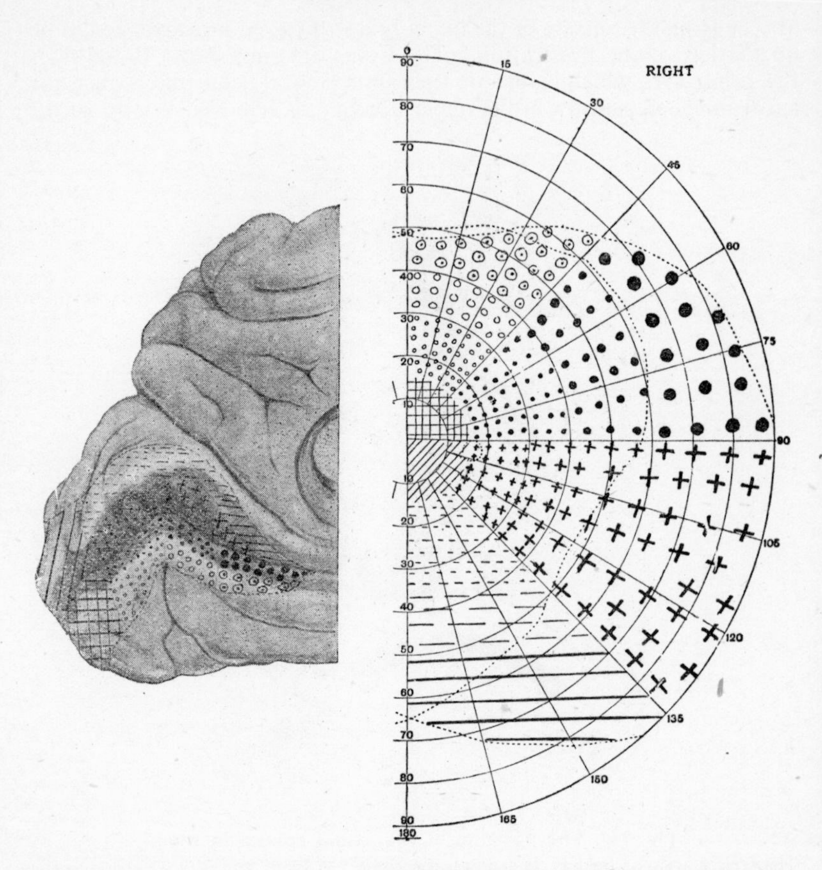

Fig. 95. Correspondence between visual field and cerebral cortex in man.

On the left the striate area of the left hemisphere of the brain is shown, the calcarine fissure being opened up to reveal that portion of it which lines its walls. On the right is the right half of one visual field. The similarity of the markings indicate the correspondence between the different segments of the visual field and the different parts of the visual cortex. See text.

(From Holmes (3), *Proc. Roy. Soc.* B, **132,** 348, 1945.)

On the left of Fig. 95 the striate area of the left hemisphere is shown, the calcarine fissure being opened up to reveal that portion of it which lines its walls. On the right of the figure is the right half of one visual field. The correspondence of the markings indicates the points of the cortex corresponding to the various parts of the visual field.

Bearing in mind that the image of the visual field is inverted on the retina, the general correspondence between retinal points and cortical points may best be understood, perhaps, by picturing one half of a retina spread over the surface of a striate area, certain parts of the retina being stretched more than others, somewhat as follows: the foveal region will be placed posteriorly at the occipital tip, the peripheral region anteriorly, the upper retinal margin along the upper edge of the striate area and the lower margin on the inferior border of the striate area. " Stretching " of the retina will be greatest for the foveal and macular regions of the retina. The cortical regions receiving the fibres originating from these more important regions of the retina are proportionately much larger than those connected with the peripheral areas of the retina.

It is possible to record the electrical changes occurring in the cortex of an animal, e.g. a monkey, when the retina of its eye is stimulated at various points by a light spot. Experiments of this kind show a correspondence between brain and retina of the same kind as that known to exist in man; the visual region of the monkey's cortex has a different shape from that of man (3).

There is thus a point-to-point correspondence between the retina and the cerebral cortex, and there is naturally a similar correspondence between the retina and the intermediate levels of the visual path such as the lateral geniculate bodies. This correspondence is somewhat like that between a map and a tracing of it made on a sheet of rubber which is subsequently stretched and folded in various ways.

SOME DETAILS OF MICROSCOPICAL ANATOMY

There is only one relay station on the way from the retina to the cortex, namely the lateral geniculate bodies. Microscopical studies have shown the nature of the connections between the fibres of the optic nerve and the fibres of the optic radiations in these bodies. The diagram of Fig. 96 shows the termination of the optic nerve fibres in relation to the cells of the lateral geniculate bodies in a monkey. A fasciculus of optic fibres (*a*) is shown entering the geniculate body from the right. Each fibre ends in a spray of 5–6 branches and each of these terminates in an end bulb or bouton which lies in contact with the body of one geniculate cell (these cells are drawn in dotted lines). The axons, or nerve fibres, of the geniculate cells (*b*) then go to the cortex, forming the optic radiation. In no case was more than one bouton found in contact with one geniculate cell. There is therefore no overlap. The nervous

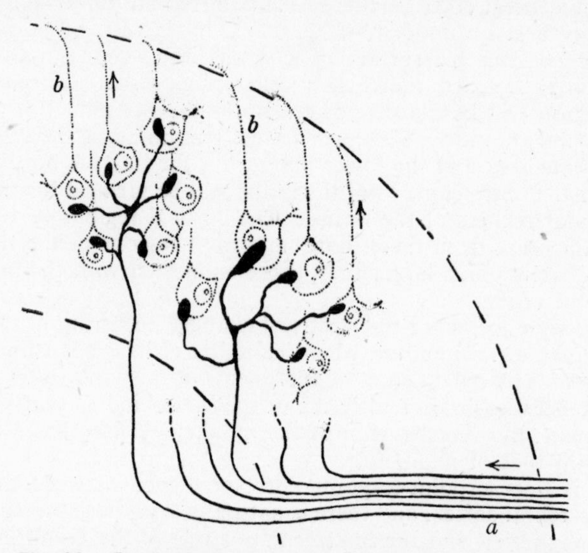

Fig. 96. Connexions in the lateral geniculate bodies.
Diagram showing the termination of optic fibres in relation to the cells of the lateral geniculate body in a monkey. See text. High magnification.
(From Glees and Clark, *J. Anat.*, **75**, 301, 1941 (5).)

stimulation transmitted along one fibre of the optic nerve can be transmitted only to the 5 or 6 fibres of the optic striations which are in connexion with its terminal boutons. These 5 or 6 fibres are unaffected by the stimulation of other optic nerve fibres. This is perfectly in keeping with the point-to-point correspondence found between retina and cortex

Crossed fibres, coming from the eye on the other side, and uncrossed fibres, coming from the eye on the same side, end in the same geniculate body. Two groups of optic radiation fibres connected one to a crossed and the other to an uncrossed fibre of the optic nerve end in the same point of the cortex, if they correspond to the same point of the visual fields. It is apparent, therefore, that by means of the geniculate body crossed and uncrossed retinal nerve impulses are brought into close relation in the cortex. This is clearly important from the point of view of binocular vision. There is no evidence, however, that the crossed and uncrossed nervous paths then really fuse into a common final path, and there are theoretical reasons why this should not be assumed.

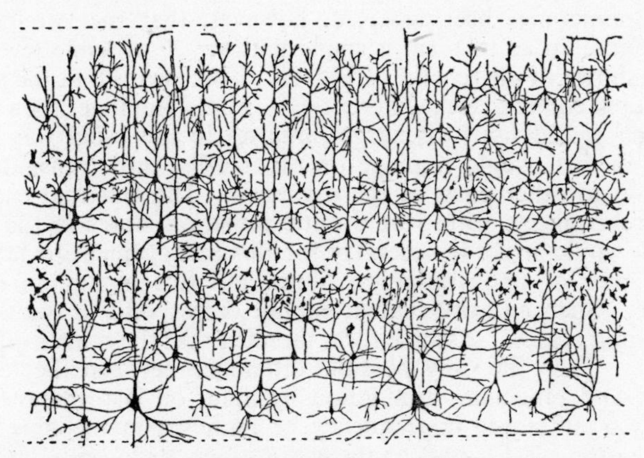

Fig. 97. Microscopic anatomy of the visual cortex.
Diagram of a section through the visual cortex of a monkey's brain. See text. High magnification.
(From Clark, *J. Anat.*, **76**, 371, 1942 (5).)

Fig. 97 shows a magnified diagrammatic section through the visual cortex of a monkey's brain. A little below the middle of the diagram, there is a horizontal layer, called the *granular layer*, which is composed of cells different from those above and below it. There is evidence that fibres of the optic radiation arising in the lateral geniculate bodies end at least for the most part in this granular layer. How exactly the optic radiation fibres are connected with the cells of the cortex, and how the nervous stimulation they transmit is propagated inside the cortex, and from there to motor nerve centres which set the muscles in action, are problems about which little is known (5).

WHY THE CROSSED AND UNCROSSED PATHS SHOULD NOT BE EXPECTED TO FUSE

As we have seen, the anatomical evidence is that the two nervous paths originating from corresponding points of the retina remain independent of one another until they reach the cortex. In the cortex, the pathways originating in the two eyes come very close to one another, but the actual connexions are not known.

It has sometimes been asserted, however, that the two pathways actually unite so as to form a single pathway *F* at some level in the brain, as shown in the scheme of Fig. 98. This means that the impulses in two fibres coming from different eyes would impinge upon a single cell, which would itself discharge impulses in the usual way. These impulses in turn would impinge on other cells, thus transmitting the stimulation to other parts of the organism. The fact that each optic nerve-fibre connects with 5 or 6 optic radiation fibres in the geniculate body would make it necessary for this arrangement to take place for each pair of optic radiation fibres, but this makes no essential difference. Such an arrangement cannot correspond to the facts, for the following reason. Assume for a moment that the scheme of Fig. 98 is correct. Then the only possible difference between the results of uniocular and binocular stimulation by light, on last analysis, would be simply a difference in frequency of impulses in the fibre *F*. By stimulating the eye *L* alone, or the eye *R* alone, or by stimulating both eyes together, it should then, theoretically, be possible to produce each time the same discharge of impulses in fibre *F*, simply by adjusting the intensity of the (stimulating) source *P*. Consequently, further reaction of the organism induced by the excitation in the fibre *F* should be independent of whether one eye or both eyes are stimulated. But in fact the reverse is true. It is a fundamental fact that the accuracy of the organism in judging distance or relief is much higher when two eyes are used than when one only is used. On these grounds it appears that the anatomical and physiological arrangement postulated above cannot be the case—though at first sight it might seem plausible.

It must be presumed that, instead of such a process of binocular summation, which would in effect defeat the purpose of binocular vision, there take place nervous processes effecting a *comparison* or *differentiation* between the stimuli coming from the two eyes, which make stereoscopic vision possible. The fact that the crossed and uncrossed paths come very close to each other in the cortex may be as useful for such processes as it would be for binocular summation.

Possible evidence from the study of the binocular threshold. Comparison of the sensitivity of a subject to light when he uses one eye only and when he uses both eyes together may give some information about the way in which the two visual tracts function together. If the schema of Fig. 98 corresponded to the facts two weak stimulations reaching the nerve cell *F* from each eye might be able to summate their action at this level and thus to reach the threshold of stimulation of this cell, while either one of them alone would be unable to do so. A stronger stimulation of the retina by light should then be necessary in the case of uniocular vision than in that of binocular vision in order to reach the threshold.

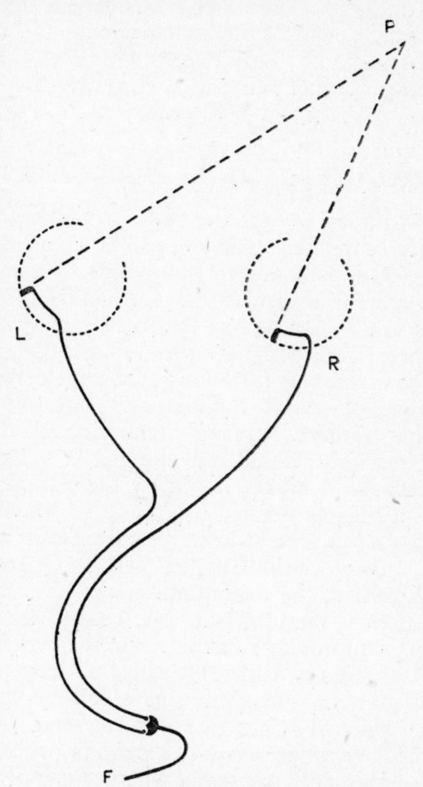

Fig. 98. Schematic imaginary arrangement of the crossed and uncrossed optic fibres.

This arrangement cannot be expected to represent the facts. See text.

Even in the case of the imaginary arrangement shown by Fig. 98, however, the two eyes might theoretically behave independently of one another, as if belonging to two different persons. This would occur if the critical barrier to be overcome by the stimulation were situated before the fusion level, *F*, of the paths coming from each eye. The barrier might be in the lateral geniculate bodies or in the retina itself.

If the theoretical objections against the schema of Fig. 98 are well founded, it must be expected that the two eyes do not summate their stimulations and behave independently. They have actually been found to act quite independently in an experiment on the absolute threshold of vision, which will be described presently. It is clear from the preceding paragraph, however, that by itself this fact is not sufficient to prove that an arrangement such as that of Fig. 98 does not exist.

BINOCULAR AND UNIOCULAR THRESHOLD OF VISION

In a dark night, we see better when we use both eyes than when we use only one. It has been known a long time that the absolute threshold, defined in terms of the brightness of the light source, is somewhat lower for binocular than for uniocular vision. The binocular threshold is not as low as one half of the uniocular, however, as it would be if there were complete physiological summation. The effect observed, therefore, was for a long time considered to be due to a kind of incomplete binocular summation. For one had the mistaken impression that if there were no summation at all, the binocular and uniocular thresholds would be the same. This conclusion is unwarranted because it makes implicitly the wrong assumption that the threshold is a sharply defined brightness at which the light is always seen, while it is never seen at lower brightnesses.

It was seen in Chapter VIII on Quantum Fluctuations that, near the threshold, the magnitude of the physical stimulus acting on the retina varies at random from one trial to the next even when conditions are kept rigorously constant. On the experimental side, it is an established fact that a considerable range of decreasing brightness must be covered to go from a brightness at which the light is almost always seen to one at which it is practically never seen. At any brightness of this intermediate range, there is a definite probability of seeing the light, but it is impossible to predict whether or not it will be seen in any particular trial.

As a basis for the explanation which follows, it must be clearly understood that the subject of the threshold experiments, when he uses both eyes, is quite unable to report whether he has seen the light with both eyes or with one eye only, and in the latter case, *a fortiori*, to report whether it was the right or the left eye. It can be surmised, therefore, that the subject reports " not seen " only when *neither* eye is stimulated; while he reports " seen " when his left eye is stimulated alone, when his right eye is stimulated alone, and when both eyes are stimulated together. For this reason he has a greater chance of reporting " seen " when he uses both eyes, even if there is no co-operation between the two eyes. What this chance is will now be calculated.

Let us call brightness threshold the brightness at which the probability of the light being seen is 50 per cent. The probability of not seeing the light at this brightness is also 50 per cent. If this refers to the use of one eye only, the probability of missing when two eyes are used together is $0{\cdot}50 \times 0{\cdot}50 = 0{\cdot}25$, *if the two eyes act independently of one another*. The probability of seeing the light while using both eyes, therefore, would then be $1 - 0{\cdot}25 = 0{\cdot}75$ at the brightness where it is seen, using one eye alone, with a probability of only 50 per cent. (6). In order to reach the brightness defined as the binocular threshold, at which the binocular probability of seeing has come down to 0·50, we therefore have to go to a brightness lower than that defined as the uniocular threshold. Thus, even in the absence of any summation, the binocular threshold must be lower than the uniocular because the probability of one eye being stimulated is greater when the subject uses two eyes than when he uses only one.

Fig. 99 represents the results of experiments using conditions similar to those used for the measurement of the minimum energy necessary for vision (7). These are a small peripheral field illuminated for a short time, and placed this time below the fixation point, at an angular distance of 20°. The three points on the ordinate corresponding to a logarithm of the brightness equal to 1·0 may be first considered. At this brightness the left eye sees the flash in 20 per cent., the right in 26 per cent., and both eyes together in 38 per cent. of the trials. On the other hand, the binocular frequency of seeing, calculated for these data on a pure probability basis, is $1 - (1 - 0{\cdot}20) \times (1 - 0{\cdot}26) = 0{\cdot}40$, which is in good agreement with the experimental value 0·38. Curve *B* of the figure is the theoretical curve giving the frequency of seeing the light calculated in the same manner, point by point, in terms of the uniocular curves *R* and *L* for the right and left eyes respectively. The agreement with the experimental data is satisfactory.

It will be noted that the binocular frequency-of-seeing curve is steeper than the uniocular curve, and that the point corresponding to 50 per cent. frequency of seeing is situated about 0·10 logarithmic unit lower than the corresponding point on the uniocular curve. The conclusion is that the absolute threshold is lower by about 20 per cent., and is more sharply defined, when the subject uses two eyes than when he uses only one. But this does not imply any summation of stimulation between the two eyes. It would occur in the same way if the experiment were made with two eyes belonging to two different people, the light being considered as "seen" when at least one of the subjects has seen it.

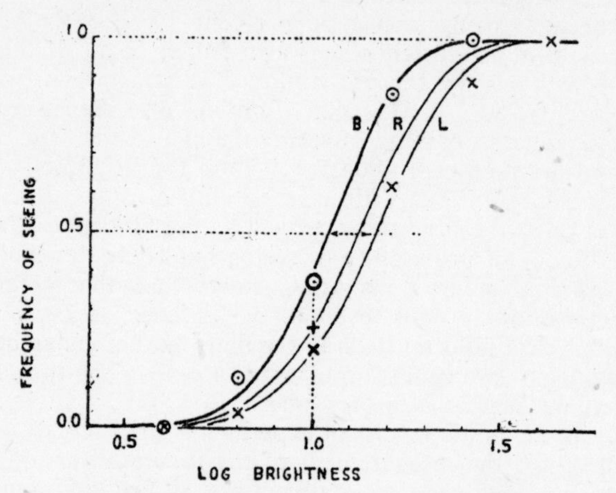

Fig. 99. Binocular and uniocular sensitivity.
Frequency of seeing, using one eye only, and using both eyes. See text.
⊙ both eyes ; + right eye ; × left eye.
(From Pirenne (7), *Nature*, **152**, 698, 1943.)

BIBLIOGRAPHY AND NOTES

(1) HELMHOLTZ, H. v. (1896). *Handbuch der Physiologische Optik*, 2nd ed., Hamburg and Leipzig.

(2) See also: RANSON, S. W. (1943). *The Anatomy of the Nervous System*, 7th ed., Philadelphia and London, and ref. (2) of Chapter I.

(3) HOLMES, G. (1945). "The organization of the visual cortex in man," *Proc. Roy. Soc. B.*, **132**, 348-361.

(4) When the entire optic radiation is cut on one side central vision is sometimes spared, as shown in Fig. 91, *G*. The reasons for this occurrence are not well understood. See ref. (2).

(5) See: CLARKE, W. E. Le Gros (1942). "The Anatomy of Cortical Vision," *Trans. Ophthalm. Soc.*, **62**, 229-245.

(6) The analogy of tossing may again be used here. "Heads" replaces "seeing" and "tails" replaces "missing." If one coin only is tossed the probability of having heads or tails is $\frac{1}{2}$. If two coins are tossed together, the probability of having tails in both is $\frac{1}{2} \times \frac{1}{2} = \frac{1}{4}$ because the two coins are assumed to be independent. The probability of not having tails for both coins is then $1 - \frac{1}{4} = \frac{3}{4}$. This is of course the probability of having heads at least for one of the coins. It corresponds to the probability of seeing at least with one of the eyes.

(7) PIRENNE, M. H. (1943). "Binocular and uniocular threshold of vision," *Nature, Lond.*, **152**, 698.

Similar conclusions for the case of binocular acuity in daylight have been reached independently by:

BÁRÁNY, E. (1946). "A theory of binocular visual acuity and an analysis of the variability of visual acuity," *Acta Ophthalm.*, **24**, 63–92.

See also theoretical considerations, and striking experiments on binocular flicker, in:

SHERRINGTON, Ch. (1906). *The Integrative Action of the Nervous System.* New ed. 1947, Cambridge. Several leading ideas used in the present book come from this physiological classic.

Chapter XVII

PHYSICS AND THE PHENOMENA OF LIFE

THE preceding chapters have shown some results of the application of the physiological method to the study of the visual system. Among other things, the remarkable efficiency of the eye as an instrument has been discussed; some important problems which are as yet unsolved have been pointed out. In this, our last chapter, it may be worth while examining briefly what general relations these studies bear to broader fields of enquiry.

It has been the commonly accepted view of physicists for a long time that an intelligence vast enough, knowing for a given instant the positions and velocities of all the particles constituting the physical universe, would be able to calculate the positions and velocities of these particles, that is, the state of the universe, at any other instant of the past or of the future. Such a statement would have to be considerably modified to be adapted to the standpoint of modern physics, according to which, among other difficulties, perfectly exact knowledge and prediction of such a kind is impossible. The statement nevertheless gives an idea of the physicist's view of the universe. He sees it as constituted of matter and energy and tries to understand its structure and changes in terms of the physical laws of matter and energy.

It is naturally possible to study living organisms, including man, from this point of view, i.e., considering an organism as a special system made up of matter and energy, included in the general system of the physical universe. It will be worth while examining later the implications of such a method of approach, and the meaning of the results it leads to. At the moment the method itself is worth examining more closely.

Within the terms of such a method, only motions such as mechanical movements, and changes such as absorption and emission of energy, electrical changes, chemical reactions, are to be considered. (It is to be borne in mind that chemical reactions, for instance, may be explained by physical interaction between molecules; such at any rate is the aim of modern chemistry.) Concepts such as sensation, feeling, thought, are not taken into consideration in such a representation of living organisms but what is sometimes called their " physical manifestation "—for instance, the laryngeal, labial and other movements occurring in speech, —fall within its scope.

If a scientist could account for all the actions of a given individual in terms of the laws of physics alone, he would be the greatest of physiologists. In doing so in terms of physics, he would necessarily disregard all considerations of mind or intelligence. This is in fact the physiological method of approach.

Physiology as a science considers the organism as a physical mechanism in the most general sense of the term, and deals only with what it regards as, in last analysis, physical processes.

When such concepts as sensation, or consciousness are mentioned in physiological works, either this is done as a mere manner of speech, or it is because physiology strictly is abandoned for psychology or philosophy (1). In the present work, words like " vision," " seeing," are used, but only as a manner of speech. They should, in strict accord with physiological method, be replaced by more cumbersome phrases such as " the reaction of photo-receptors and nervous system to certain electro-magnetic radiations." Similarly when a phrase such as " blue light " is used for the sake of brevity it means in fact " electro-magnetic radiation having a wave-length in the neighbourhood of 450mμ." Such radiation falling into my eye under suitable conditions, is capable of making me say that I see a blue object. But it has been seen that such " blue light " in conditions of rod vision will make me say that I see a gray or white object.

Physiology as a science does not deny that there are conscious sensations and cognitive reactions: it simply does not deal with them. It makes, as this book has made, a consistent attempt to deal only with physical reactions and processes. In the matching experiments used in studying colour vision, for instance, the aim is to determine, not what colours the subject sees, but only whether two illuminated fields act differently on his eye or not. Psychological problems of perception do not arise simply because they have been left outside the limits of physiological enquiry, as defined in the introduction. Such a problem, for example, is: why do we *see* things as continuous wholes instead of as a mosaic of discrete stimulations corresponding to the retinal mosaic of receptors?

Physiology, like physics, has so far been considered here only as a method of approach to the study of the world. Now, even assuming that the tasks of physics and physiology were fulfilled, that they had solved all their problems, the body of knowledge so obtained could not be considered as an adequate description of the universe and of the organisms in it. For it would have left out of account all mind or consciousness, including the consciousness of the physiologist or the physicist. As has often been pointed out, this is the impasse which faces any philosophy of pure materialism: if only matter exists, then there is no mind, no intelligence, no knowledge, no philosophy; any speaking or writing is mere meaningless muscular movements. If physiology is the whole truth, then physiology itself becomes a mere collection of particles in motion.

There can be no experimental proof that physiology gives the whole truth about the organism. For from its very terms of reference physiology deals only with the processes of the organism of which it can study the physical aspects. Consequently it can never find anything else—the mind itself will never be seen under the scalpel of the scientists—but it is not entitled to say: there is nothing else to be found.

The problem of the relation between physiological process and mental phenomenon is the great time-honoured problem of the relation of mind and body. Sensory physiology cannot solve this philosophical problem, precisely because it studies only one term of the relation: the body. Physics is not the key to the minds of men; neither is physiology.

BIBLIOGRAPHY

(1) "There are no physiological sensations, images, or ideas." See this point discussed by a psychologist: F. C. BARTLETT (1932). *Remembering. A study in experimental and social psychology*, p. 234. Cambridge.

See also: PIRENNE, M. H. (1947). "On Physiology and Consciousness," *Brit. J. Psychology*, **37**, Pt. 2, 82–86.

WOODGER, J. H. (1929). *Biological Principles*, London.

INDEX